CANADA

UNITED STATES

MEXICO

CENTRAL AMERICA

SOUTH AMERICA

4

3

I

2

Routes followed by
MIGRATING BIRDS

1. Mostly water birds take this
   long route.

2. Some birds fly over Cuba.

3. Most birds take this route.

4. Swallows and day migrants
   go through Mexico.

D1243931

85

From
Mrs. Dean S. Luce
Christmas 1943

What? More WORMS? A mother Robin has
to work hard to feed her hungry children.

# from Robin to Junco

STORIES OF BIRDS AND WHAT THEY DO

BY

## MARY I. CURTIS

ILLUSTRATED BY

LEMUEL PALMER AND JEROME DONOVAN

HOUGHTON MIFFLIN COMPANY

Boston · New York · Chicago · Dallas · Atlanta · San Francisco

The Riberside Press Cambridge

The Riverside Press
CAMBRIDGE · MASSACHUSETTS
PRINTED IN THE U.S.A.

To
HARRY C. OWENS

Without whose help
this book
would never have
been written

# Contents

v

# Acknowledgments

*Grateful acknowledgment is made to Professor Arthur A. Allen of Cornell University for permission to reproduce his color photographs which appear in this book; and to National Geographic Magazine for the loan of three of Professor Allen's photographs first published in that magazine.*

# List of Color Photographs

BY ARTHUR A. ALLEN

## A Walk in the Woods

BIRDS fly," said Ann.

"What else do they do?" asked the tall man, smiling down at the little girl beside him.

"They sing."

"Anything else?"

Ann took a longer time to answer this question. She looked down at the ground and tried to think. At last she said,

"They lay eggs, and — and — robins eat worms."

1

"Is that all they do?"

Once more Ann tried to think, pulling gently at a lock of her thick hair as if by doing so she might, perhaps, pull forth an answer to the tall man's question.

Then she looked up and laughed.

"I can't think of anything else just now," she said. "I guess I don't know very much about birds, Uncle Jim. You'll have to tell me what they do."

Uncle Jim laughed with her.

"You live in the city," he said. "You haven't had as much chance to watch birds, as if you'd been out here in the country where there are plenty of trees and shrubs for them to nest in. But you're going to be a country girl all this long vacation, and you'll know a lot about all kinds of birds before you go back home in the fall. You'll learn to like them, too, I think, as well as you like other animals."

"I like them now," said Ann, "only I don't know much about them. They seem so different — flying around up in the air — from animals on the ground. They don't seem to have much to do with us."

The tall man and the little girl had been walking along a country road, but now they stopped beside an old log which lay in the shade of some trees at the side of the road.

"Let's sit down here," said the man. "There might be some birds in the trees around about here, and we can see what they are doing. You may find that they are not so different, after all, from the animals that live on the ground."

They sat down quietly and tried to keep as still as if they themselves were trees. They didn't want to frighten any bird that might come near.

Suddenly they heard a little rush and flutter of wings. A mother Robin, carrying a fat angle-worm in her bill, lit on the edge of a nest almost hidden by the leaves and branches of a tree close beside them.

"Don't move," said Uncle Jim in a low voice, and Ann sat as motionless as a little statue while she watched.

The Robin cocked her head on one side and eyed them with suspicion in her beady black eye. But as they made no sound or motion, the mother bird decided everything was all right, and she began to feed the worm to the three, wide, open mouths of the baby Robins in the nest. She put her bill with the delicious food so far down into each of the baby's mouths that it seemed almost as if she would choke them. But they liked it and promptly opened their bills wide again, asking for more.

As the last bit of worm was eaten the mother Robin, with a flash of her wings, was off again to hunt a new supply of food.

"You see," said Uncle Jim, "That mother Robin has to feed and take care of her children just as other mothers do. She works hard, too, and worries over her babies for fear something may harm them. That's why she looked at us so sharply. She was afraid we might be up to some mischief."

"She looked as if she'd like to tell us to go home," said Ann. "I guess birds aren't so different from other animals as I thought they were."

"That's right," said Uncle Jim. "We're so used to taking them for granted as just birds, that we're not apt to think much about the way they live and what they do.

"But, after all, a bird like other animals, works and plays, has pleasures and troubles, and fears

4

and dangers. Its concerns are as important to the bird as ours are to us. It is happy when the sun shines and when it has enough to eat, and it is sad and hungry too, sometimes, just as we often are."

"I never thought about that," said Ann, looking up through the branches at the Robin's nest. A hungry *cheep, cheep, cheep* told her that the baby birds were calling for *more food, more food, more WORMS!* "But I still don't see that they have much to do with us."

The day was warm and the sun shone hotly on the road, but under the trees the shade of the green leaves was cool and pleasant. Uncle Jim looked around him.

"It's nice here under the shade of the trees, isn't it?" he said.

"It's lovely," Ann agreed.

"You like trees, don't you, Ann?"

"Why, yes, of course I do." She looked at Uncle Jim a little puzzled. "But we were talking about birds, weren't we?"

"Birds and trees go together," said her uncle. "If we had no birds we might not have the shade of any of these trees to enjoy."

Ann's brown eyes popped wide open with surprise.

"Why, Uncle Jim, what do you mean?"

"Because there are millions and millions and billions of harmful little bugs and worms that feed on trees and on other plants too. If the birds didn't hunt them out and eat them, many of the trees would die. Listen! ..."

He stopped suddenly and held up his hand. "There's a Woodpecker near here now — rapping on a tree. Hear him?"

From somewhere not far away there came a quick *rat-tat-tat-tat-tat! rat-tat-tat-tat-tat!* as if someone were tapping rapidly with a stick upon a piece of wood.

6

Then as suddenly as it had begun, the sound stopped, and out into the open flashed a gay and beautiful bird. It had a bright red head, like a crimson hood, and a body of sharply contrasted black and white.

"See him! There he goes!" said Uncle Jim. "A Red-headed Woodpecker. Isn't he a beauty!"

# The Upside-down Bird

DOES the Red-headed Woodpecker eat bugs?" asked Ann.

"Oh, yes, he's greedy for them.  He likes wild nuts and fruit pretty well.  But he's very, very fond of grasshoppers and flies and little beetles that bore deep down into the bark and trunk of trees.

"His cousins, the Hairy Woodpecker and the little Downy Woodpecker, do even better than he does in the matter of destroying tree bugs. They eat thousands and thousands of insects and worms and grubs.

8

The Downy Woodpecker eats insects and bugs that kill trees.

The Bluebird helps too. He eats grasshoppers and other insects that harm our gardens.

"All Woodpeckers have strong, sharp bills. They can peck and drill into a tree and dig out insects that are so deeply hidden in the wood that other birds can't reach them easily. Woodpeckers help to save many trees.

"The modest little Brown Creeper isn't so showy as the Woodpeckers, but he does his part too. Creeping up a tree from the very roots, he carefully picks out all the little insects and insect eggs he can find for his dinner. He gives the trunk and branches a careful going over. When he reaches the top he flies off to another tree and starts all over again. He has a big appetite."

*Downy Woodpecker*

*Brown Creeper*

9

"Does he know he's saving the trees?" asked Ann.

"No, I don't suppose he does, but he saves them just the same."

For a minute or so Uncle Jim sat quietly without saying anything. Then he went on talking.

"And there is the busy little White-breasted Nuthatch. He helps, too. Sometimes he's called the 'Upside-down Bird.' You can't fail to know him when you've once seen him, because he works in a very odd fashion. It doesn't seem to bother him a bit to stand on his head. And when he lights on a tree he travels all the way down the branches and the trunk, head first and upside down from top to root, taking out all the insects that the other birds missed, or didn't like.

"He looks under every piece of bark and into every little crack where a bug or worm might be hiding. He doesn't intend to miss any tasty morsel if he can help it.

"He isn't in a hurry. He travels straight ahead without stopping to look around him, and as he goes he keeps up a funny little call of *yank, yank, yank, yank*, always in the same tone.

"The White-breasted Nuthatch has two little

cousins, the Red-breasted Nuthatch and the Pygmy Nuthatch. They are smaller than their white-breasted cousin but their habits are much the same, especially their upside-down habits. There is a third cousin too, the Brown-headed Nuthatch. But he lives in the South most of the time."

Uncle Jim shifted his position on the log and found a comfortable tree to lean against. He stretched his long legs out in front of him and went on talking.

"And while we are thinking of birds that save the trees, we mustn't for- get the Black and White Warbler — such a restless, busy little bird! He creeps along the trunk and bran- ches of a tree, hunting for insects in about the same way a Brown Creeper does. And, very much like  the Nuthatches, he too goes both up and down a tree, showing that he can do what both the other birds can do.

"But though the Black and White Warbler and

the Nuthatches are the only birds that creep down a tree as well as up, the Warbler is different from the Nuthatches because in his going he has a much more jerky movement. He hops from one tree to another, always on the jump. And every time he hops he faces in a different direction.

"The Black and White Warbler is much more easily seen than the Brown Creeper and the Nuthatches because he wears a showy coat of striped black and white."

"I'd like to see an Upside-down Bird, or a Black and White Warbler," said Ann.

"You will some day, if you watch. They come around here often. But there..." Uncle Jim broke off suddenly and pointed to a little tree across the road in front of them. "There is something for you to see, right now."

About ten or twelve little gray and black birds had lighted on the tree. In the happiest, most care-free manner you could imagine, they were hopping around clinging to the ends of branches and swinging from the ends of little twigs in all sorts of positions. And as they hopped about they kept up, all the time, a cheery musical chatter of *dee-dee-dee*.

"Oh!" whispered Ann, drawing a long breath. "Oh, aren't they cunning! What kind are they?"

"They are Chickadees, Black-capped Chickadees. See the little black feather caps they wear on their heads? They are the friendliest little birds in all the world. Listen... They have named themselves, and they are always repeating their names, *Chick-a-dee-dee-dee, dee-dee-dee.*

"They aren't as afraid of people as most of the birds are. In fact, they seem to be quite curious about us queer unfeathered human beings. They do good work, too, because their food is made up almost entirely of small insects and insect eggs that they find far out on the little twigs and leaves, where the larger birds can't perch, but where the smaller Chickadees can light.

"Chickadees don't mind cold weather. They stay here all winter. And even in the winter they are doing good, for when crawling and flying insects can't be found, these cheery little birds can still find the bugs and insect eggs that are hidden in the bark of trees and other places."

"They look as if they were having a good time, don't they?" said Ann.

Uncle Jim laughed. "They look to me like a lot of hungry little boys on a picnic, jumping around and playing while they are eating their sandwiches.

"The Chickadee belongs to the Titmouse family, and he has a cousin, the Tufted Titmouse, who behaves in much the same way as the

Chickadee. The Tufted Titmouse has a pointed crest of feathers on his head, but he is about the same size as the Chickadee, and he scrambles around searching for his food among little branches and twigs that wouldn't be strong enough to support a larger bird. He swings from the ends of twigs perfectly at ease in any sort of position, right side up, upside down, or sideways.

"Titmice like to hunt in groups. You will often see a whole flock of them together peering into little cracks in the bark of some tree, looking for insects to eat. Sometimes a little Titmouse will light on a twig that is hardly big enough to hold him up. But he holds on any old way in order to pick off the tiny insects or insect eggs for his dinner.

"The Brown Creepers, the Nuthatches, the Downy Woodpeckers, the little Chickadees, and the Titmice like each others' company. Sometimes, especially in the fall and winter, you can see them all together on one tree.

"And along with them you'll often see the tiny Golden-crowned Kinglet and his relative, the Ruby-crowned Kinglet. They help their friends in the work of bug hunting and eating.

15

"The Kinglets like to hunt in shrubs and bushes along the banks of brooks.

"These little Kinglets are almost the smallest of our native birds, except, of course, the Hummingbirds. But what they lack in size they more than make up for in energy. They bounce around among the branches like little rubber balls."

While Uncle Jim and Ann had been watching the birds, time had been slipping along. The sun was almost overhead. Uncle Jim looked up at it. Then he looked at his watch and jumped up from the log.

"Come," he said, "It's dinner time. Aren't you hungry?"

Ann sat still.

"It's so nice here," she said. "The trees look different to me now from the way they did when we first came, and I'd like to see the Robin feed her babies once more."

"The birds will take care of the trees," said Uncle Jim, "but they won't give us our dinner. If you were a young Robin I could feed you a worm, but I think you'd rather have a different sort of dinner."

He reached down his hand and pulled Ann to her feet.

"Besides," he added, "birds don't fly around very much in the middle of the day. They like to rest then. We'll see some more tomorrow."

*Birds and trees go together.*

# Father Robin and the Worm

THE next morning, as soon as Ann saw Uncle Jim, she suggested another trip to the woods.

"I'd like to see the Robin's nest again," she said.

Uncle Jim had just finished his breakfast. He folded his napkin and laid it beside his plate.

"So you want to go back to the woods," he said. "Did you dream the Robin's nest had gone, or that bugs had eaten all the trees?"

Ann looked thoughtful.

18

"No . . ." she said slowly. "But I did think about it, and I should like to see that Robin's nest again."

"If it's just a Robin's nest you want to see, you won't have to go all the way to the woods to see it," said Uncle Jim pushing his chair back from the table and standing up. "There's one in a tree right at the end of the porch.

"If we move quietly, we won't frighten the mother bird. She's quite friendly, and she has been here so long that she's used to us. The young Robins must be nearly old enough to leave the nest."

When Uncle Jim and Ann came out on the porch, they could see one of the young Robins sitting up on the edge of the nest. It had grown so big that there was hardly room enough for it and the other young birds inside. Every few minutes it would flap its wings a little, as if it were trying to keep from falling.

"Why, how big he is!" exclaimed Ann. "And he doesn't have a red breast like a Robin, at all. He's all spotted."

"A young Robin always has a spotted breast when he gets his first feathers. By the time his breast turns red, he calls himself quite grown up, though he is full size long before that time. He ought to be big enough, certainly, because he eats so much. It keeps both Father Robin and Mother Robin busy hunting all day long to find food enough for their children.

"Mother Robin has other things to do besides supplying food all the time. First she has to build her nest. I watched her build this one. I wish you could have seen how carefully and skillfully she wove little stalks and grasses together. Then she plastered them with mud, and shaped the nest by pressing her breast against it from the inside as she built it.

"Taking care of her eggs and of the newly hatched babies is real work. Later on, she has to look out for the young birds while they are learning to fly, and she has to show them where to find food for themselves. Though they look big, the young Robins are still just hungry babies when they are first out of the nest. But once out of it, they never go back again.

"I saw an amusing bit of Robin family life one day last summer. A mother Robin was hopping around on the ground hunting worms to feed a big, young Robin that was hopping along right behind her.

"Every once in a while Mother Robin would cock her head sideways, with one ear toward the ground, as if she were listening for a radio signal from below.

"When she got the right station, Station WORM, she would dig her bill quickly into the ground and pull out a nice juicy angleworm. Then she would turn and feed the choice bit into the always ready bill of her hungry child.

"One time, however, she got hold of an especially long, fat worm. She started to pull it out of the ground. But the worm had other ideas.

It didn't wish to be anybody's dinner, and it wouldn't let go of the ground.

"Mother Robin pulled and pulled, and then braced herself and tugged and tugged. She got the worm about half way out of the ground, but the rest of it just would not come.

"Finally she realized that this was going to be too much for her, and spying Father Robin also worm hunting near by, she let go of the angle-worm and called to him to come and help her.

"You should have seen Father Robin. He came hurrying over with a most important air, as if he were saying, 'Now, just leave this to me, Mother Robin. It needs a man to handle this kind of thing. I'll show you how it ought to be done.'

"And he did. He caught hold of the end of that angleworm and with a strong, quick jerk, he pulled the whole worm completely out of the ground.

"Oh, then was he pleased with himself! He stood there with his red breast all puffed out with pride, holding his head up in the air with the angleworm dangling from his bill, to show Mother Robin how clever and how strong he was.

22

"But — just in the moment of his triumph a bold little English Sparrow slipped up from behind, snatched the worm right out of Father Robin's bill and flew away with it."

"Oh, poor Father Robin!" exclaimed Ann. "What happened then? Did he get it back?"

"No. Looking very much annoyed, Father Robin hopped back to what he had been doing when Mother Robin called him, and Mother Robin tactfully pretended not to notice. She just went on hunting for another worm as if nothing unusual had happened."

# A Messenger of Spring

WHAT color do you like best, Ann?" asked Uncle Jim, as he finished feeding the birds in the back yard.

Ann, who had run out to watch him, looked down at her new dress.

"I like blue," she said, "the color of this dress I'm wearing." She smoothed it down a little at the sides. "It's new.... Don't you think it's pretty?"

"I think it's just about exactly right." Uncle Jim put his hand on her shoulder and turned her slowly around. "Just about the best I've ever seen."

They both laughed and Uncle Jim leaned over to pick up the empty basket.

"Well, that's all for the birds this time," he said.

He turned the basket upside down to shake out the last crumbs.

"I like to have the birds come to eat on our lawn," he told Ann. "It's fun to watch them, and it makes things easier for the mother bird, too. Several birds have nests near by, and while they are busy taking care of their eggs or their young birds, I think they may be glad to find a bird cafeteria so handy.

"And now that I've found out you like blue, I'm going to show you a Bluebird." He smiled at her. "You look a little like a Bluebird, yourself, in that blue dress. And you couldn't copy a nicer bird.

"Everybody loves the Bluebird. (See color photograph opposite page 8.) He is so cheerful and friendly. His song is sweet, and he will sing at any time, early or late, in sunshine or in rain. He never scolds or fusses or makes a loud noise, as some of the other birds do. In fact, his cheery song and his pleasant manners have won for the Bluebird the name of 'Bird of Happiness,' and he is supposed to bring good luck to the place where he makes his home.

"Bluebirds like sheltered nests. They will nest quite close to a barn or house if a comfortable birdhouse is put up for them.

"We had some Bluebirds that nested for several years in an old dead tree near the barn. The tree was so old we were afraid it would be blown over on the barn by a wind storm sometime.

"We hated to cut it down, though, because if we did the Bluebirds' nest would be destroyed. But after a while the time came when we didn't dare leave the old tree standing any longer.

"Before we cut the dead tree down, however, we built a nice little birdhouse for the Bluebirds, which we hoped would take the place of their old home. We fastened it in the branches of a little tree near by." Uncle Jim pointed to a tree near the barn. "There it is right beside that old dead stump."

"Did the Bluebirds like the new house, Uncle Jim?"

"I should say they did. We hadn't much more than placed it in the tree and climbed down to the ground again, before they were flying around looking over the new house and deciding to move in. They settled there right away, and they've been coming back to this same house, ever since.

"Let's go over quietly and see if any Bluebirds are there now." He took Ann's hand. "Walk slowly and don't make any quick motions to frighten them."

Hand in hand Ann and Uncle Jim walked toward the barn. Sure enough, there was a Bluebird perched high on a branch of the tree. He was a lovely sight with his bright blue head and back and wings against the green leaves of the tree.

"But, look!" whispered Ann. "He has a red breast just like a Robin."

"Oh, yes. The Bluebird is a cousin of the Robin and he has a perfect right to have a red breast, too. Bluebirds and Robins both belong to the Thrush family. A young Bluebird, just like a young Robin, always has a spotted breast before he gets his grown-up coloring.

"There are several other kinds of Thrushes, besides the Robin and the Bluebird. The spotted breast of all the young birds is a family trait."

At that moment the Bluebird decided they had looked at him long enough. With a gay, warbling song he flew away toward the road.

"Oh, I like him!" exclaimed Ann. "He's the prettiest bird I've seen yet."

"And he's just as gentle and good as he is pretty. Bluebirds don't do any harm to grain or fruit or gardens. Instead of harm they do good, because they eat grasshoppers and beetles and other insects that would hurt the gardens.

"The Bluebird is the first real messenger of spring — even a truer messenger than his cousin, the Robin, because some Robins stay on in the North all winter. Some Bluebirds stay North, too. But Bluebirds don't like winter. Zero weather is too hard on them. Most of them go away.

"But they come back to us with the earliest spring days, even before the snow has entirely gone.

"And so, if some morning after a long winter, you should see the Bluebird's lovely color on a fence post by the roadside, and should hear his happy warble, you can be sure that winter has at last made up its mind to go, and that spring and summer are on the way."

# The Blue Jay's Bargain

ANN was helping Uncle Jim scatter bits of bread to tempt the birds to eat their supper on the lawn. She was thinking of the Bluebird she had seen the day before.

"What about the rest of the Thrush family, Uncle Jim?" she asked, looking around to see if any birds were coming for the crumbs.

"How many Thrushes are there, and do they have red breasts like the Robins and the Bluebirds?"

Uncle Jim sat down on the end of the porch and let his feet hang over as he talked.

"The other Thrush cousins are a little different," he said. "There are quite a good many of them, but they are mostly duller in color, with grayish, or olive, or russet-brown shadings. Some of them keep the spotted breasts that they all have when they are young, and all of them are a great deal more shy and timid than the Robin and the Bluebird.

"The Wood Thrush is the only one that will make his home anywhere near the homes of people.

The Wood Thrush is a cousin of the Robin and the Bluebird.

"The Blue Jay is a handsome rascal and a very cocky bird."

Sometimes one may set up housekeeping in the shrubs or shade trees near a house, but he likes the deep woods a great deal better. The other Thrushes keep themselves pretty well hidden, too.

"The Thrush cousins all differ somewhat in their habits and in their looks, but all of them sing beautifully.

"The Hermit Thrush hides in the deep woods. He keeps out of sight as much as he can, and he

*Wood Thrush*

is almost always alone. That's why he's called a hermit. The Hermit Thrush is the sweetest singer of the Thrush family. I've heard people say his song is as sweet as that of the English Nightingale, and you know, the English Nightingale is supposed to sing more beautifully than any other bird in all the world.

"The Nightingale and the Thrushes are really second cousins, anyway, even though they do live on different sides of the world.

"There are several other Thrushes that live mostly in the deep woods, away from people. One of them is the Veery. I know a story about the Veery, but I'll tell it to you some other time. It is a sort of sad story, and this is much too fine a day for a sad story. Don't you think so?"

*Bluebird*

"Yes, I guess so," agreed Ann. "But don't you know any stories that aren't sad? And aren't there any other birds as blue and pretty as the Blue-bird?"

"Oh, yes, there are several other birds with blue feathers. There is the beautiful blue, blue Indigo Bunting. He's very blue all over.

"And there is the Blue Jay. (See color photograph opposite page 30.) He's a handsome rascal and a very cocky bird, with his crested head held high and his rich blue and black and white coat. The Blue Jay wears a neat black collar, and his tail and wings are marked with bars of black and white.

*Indigo Bunting*

"But in spite of his good looks, the Blue Jay is something of a rogue. He doesn't have

33

the nice manners of the Bluebird nor the Bluebird's pleasant song.  He is a noisy creature, with a
loud, harsh, squeaky voice.  His song sounds, for
all the world, like a rusty, squeaky, pulley wheel.

"He is bigger than the Thrushes, and he belongs to an entirely different family, the Crow
family.  You know Crows, those big, black birds
that fly around screaming *caw! caw! caw!*, and
that steal the farmer's corn.  That's why the
farmers put up funny scarecrows in their fields
to scare the Crows away.  The Crows believe these
funny scarecrows are live men, and Crows are
afraid of men.

"Well, the Blue Jay is the Crow's cousin, and he will steal too, if he gets the chance. Sometimes I am sorry to say he will even take the eggs of other birds. But that is only when he has a family of young birds to feed.

"However, he is not all bad. He helps to destroy harmful insects such as grasshoppers and caterpillars and beetles. And he does another thing that is very good. He helps to plant our forests.

"Sit down here on the porch and I'll tell you a story about the Blue Jay.

"He is extremely fond of chestnuts and acorns and beechnuts. He eats a great many of these nuts, and when he has eaten all he wants at any one time, he hides a number more so that he will have a store of them laid by for another time. He tucks away hundreds of these nuts in hollow trees, and in the grass, and under fallen leaves on the ground. Then if a forest is cut down, or destroyed, there is a chance for chestnut, oak, and beech trees to grow again from these hidden nuts.

"When I was a little boy, my grandfather used to tell me that there was a bargain between the oak tree and the Blue Jay.

35

"'I grow so many acorns,' said the oak tree to the Blue Jay, 'that I have a lot to spare. Now, if you will help me to plant my acorns, I will give you all you need of them for food, and I'll let you build your nest in my branches, where I can protect you with my leaves and shade.'

"The Blue Jay agreed to this bargain, and since that time the oak tree and the Blue Jay have been friends.

"And, you know, it does seem to me sometimes, when I see the Blue Jay sailing by up in the sky, looking as if he felt he was somebody, that he is saying boastfully: 'See those fine trees! My great, great, great, great, great grandfather planted those big trees! ... And I've done my part, too!'

"Off he goes calling proudly in his harsh voice, 'See! see! see! see!'"

# A Window-Sill Drama

THERE was a clear, whistling warble and then a flash of bright red outside the kitchen window.

There was another soft whistle from inside the kitchen, and a low voice called,

"Ann, Ann, come here, and see a perfect gentleman! ... But, sh! sh! come very gently. He is a Cardinal, and shy. If he sees you move he will fly away in a wink."

Ann tiptoed softly into the kitchen and peeked

carefully through the window curtains. There she saw a beautiful, red bird perched on the edge of a little feeding tray that was fastened to the window sill outside the kitchen window.

The tray was filled with sunflower seeds that the red bird had come to eat. But he looked around him here and there first, to make sure that no danger was near. He held his bright, crested head high as if he were listening.

Ann hardly dared to breathe for fear of frightening away this lovely bird. And the listening Cardinal, seeming to feel that all was safe, gave a crisp little call.

He was answered by another call in a slightly lower tone. In a moment down flew the Cardinal's mate to join him at the feeding tray.

She was not so bright in her coloring as he was, but she was lovely in her own way, with her soft, duller feathers and her red bill.

He thought she was lovely, too. His manner showed real tenderness for her. He moved up close beside her. Then he leaned down and picked up a big sunflower seed. He shucked off the outer husk and turning his head to hers he slipped the seed gently into her bill.

Three times he did this. Then a sound from below startled them, and the two birds flew away, putting a sudden end to this little drama of affection.

Ann turned a beaming face to Uncle Jim.

"He kissed her!" she exclaimed. "Oh, weren't they lovely! You saw them do it, didn't you?"

"Well I think you might call it a bird kiss," agreed Uncle Jim. "It meant that he was very fond of her, I'm sure. Cardinals, unlike many other birds, choose their mates for life, and a Cardinal shows his mate a good deal of loving attention.

"Sometimes he tends the nest for her. Sometimes he hunts food for her. Sometimes he just sits and sings to her; and if she answers him, as she often does, he breaks out into a still more joyful song. He is, as I said, a polite gentleman, as well as a beautiful one.

"And while we are talking of red birds, there is another one you ought to know about — the Scarlet Tanager. (See color photograph opposite page 44.) He is as brilliant as the Cardinal. In fact, he is an even brighter red, set off by jet black wings and a black tail. But the Scarlet

Tanager doesn't have the manners that makes the Cardinal so charming.

"He is very shy and stays off in the woods most of the time, singing and hunting for beetles, bugs, and especially caterpillars, which he eats greedily. But when you do chance to come upon him in the shady woods you are almost startled by the dazzling brilliance of his plumage. He looks like a glowing red live coal or like a brilliant scarlet flower against the green leaves of the tree.

"The lady Tanager, though, is as dull as he is bright. You'd hardly think she was a Tanager, at all. She is just a dull olive green in color.

"Some people might suggest that he spent all the family money on his clothes and left nothing for his wife to dress up with. But he dresses in this gaudy way for a real purpose. He wants to attract attention away from his mate when she is on her nest, so that she can sit there safely, unnoticed and undisturbed to hatch her eggs and care for the young birds. In winter, after all the young birds have grown up, he puts on a dull coat, too.

"Most female birds are duller in appearance than the male birds, and this is the reason why."

"Well, I'm glad I'm not a bird then," said Ann, "because I like pretty clothes. But maybe the birds don't mind."

"No," said Uncle Jim. "They don't mind. They'd rather have it that way. They feel safer so.

"The Rose-breasted Grosbeak is a relative of the Cardinal and he has several of the Cardinal's fine qualities. He wears red, too, but not so much red as the Cardinal and the Scarlet Tanager. He is content with a sort of chest protector of soft rose red over his white breast. His head is black, and the rest of his body is black and white. His strong bill gives him the name of Grosbeak.

"And if you want to know him you will have to visit him in the wood lot, where he lives. He isn't likely to be seen around the house.

"Like the Cardinal, he is very fond of his mate and he takes good care of her when she is nesting. Sometimes he will sing a long and cheerful song to her from a tree near by, to entertain her, and sometimes he will carry a little tid-bit to feed her on the nest.

"He helps in looking out for the young birds, too, when they are growing up.

"The Grosbeak has a good deal of dignity and his nerves seem to be pretty steady. He doesn't, apparently, let little things disturb him easily, and he doesn't fly around just for the sake of flying as some of the more nervous birds do. He seems to be really going somewhere on purpose when he flies.

"Farmers think a great deal of the Grosbeak, because he eats large quantities of potato bugs. He is almost the only bird that likes to eat them.

"Once I watched a family of Grosbeaks for several days. They went every morning to a small potato field, where the vines were being so badly eaten by potato bugs that there were hardly any leaves left on them. At first just a pair of Grosbeaks came to the field, but after a day or two the parent birds brought four young birds with them when they came.

"The young birds perched in a row on the top rail of the fence beside the field. Then both of the old birds flew back and forth between the fence and the vines, picking off potato bugs and feeding them to the young birds as fast as they could gulp them down. The next day they came again and the parents fed the young birds as before.

"Several days passed, and then I went over to the field again.

"The birds had gone, but not a single potato bug was left upon the vines. The bugs had served as breakfast, lunch, and dinner for the Grosbeak family, and the birds had saved the whole potato crop."

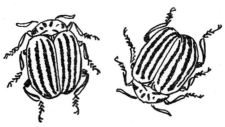

*Potato bugs*

# Feathered Yellow Gold

WOULDN'T it be lovely," said Ann, coming into the library where Uncle Jim was reading the morning paper, "if all the birds were as pretty and bright-colored as the Bluebird and the Cardinal and the Tanager?"

"Well, I don't know," answered Uncle Jim putting down the newspaper. "It seems to me that most birds have something pretty about them. But there are a good many more gay-colored birds than the ones we have been talking about."

Ann went over and leaned against the arm of his chair.

"What colors are they?" she asked. "Red or blue like the other birds?"

"There are some yellow birds," Uncle Jim replied. "The Goldfinch is one of them. He's the brightest, happiest, merriest bit of feathered, yellow gold that ever flew about in the summer sky. This sunshiny little bird sings such a sweet song, and wears such a bright, yellow coat trimmed with black wings that he is often nicknamed the Wild Canary. But he's not a Canary.

"Goldfinches are very friendly birds."

"The brilliant Scarlet Tanager stays off in the deep woods most of the time."

*Goldfinch*

"The Goldfinch is the happiest bird alive. He loves to sing, and when Mrs. Goldfinch is busy tending to her home duties, Mr. Goldfinch flies around in a wavy, up and down flight just bubbling over with song, and telling the world how happy he is.

"He doesn't seem to be going anywhere in particular when he is flying and singing in this way — dropping and rising and dropping again, swinging through the air. He is just joy-riding, like a sort of aerial roller coaster, singing as he goes.

"Goldfinches are very friendly birds. Sometimes you can hear a merry chorus of a dozen or more, all singing together at the same time. And that's something worth hearing!

"When the eggs are hatched and the young birds are in the nest, or maybe big enough to sit upon a branch, the father and mother birds bring them food. They fly around them with anxious care making soft little sounds as if to tell the new little birds that everything is all right in this new world.

"And the young Goldfinches, all nestled close together, seem to answer back *ba-by, ba-bee, ba-bee,* as if asking to be taken care of.

"You'll have a chance some day to hear a Goldfinch call. It is one of the sweetest sounds in the whole bird kingdom."

"Are there any other yellow birds, Uncle Jim?" asked Ann.

"Oh, yes, there are ever so many of them that are either yellow or partly yellow. There's the brilliant Baltimore Oriole. He's gayer in color than the Goldfinch, but his color is more orange than yellow. He has a black head and black and white wings. He's really a very handsome fellow, and his manners match his beautiful appearance.

46

"The Baltimore Oriole has a name that any bird might be proud of. I'll tell you how he came to have it.

"A long time ago, in the days of the early English settlers in America, the first Lord Baltimore made a visit to this country. He found in the woods around the shores of the Chesapeake Bay great numbers of richly colored American orioles. Lord Baltimore was so delighted with the beauty of these brilliant birds that he used their colors — orange and black — for his coat of arms.

"Sometime afterwards a famous naturalist wished to give a name to this American oriole.

47

And because the bird wore the colors of the Bal-timore family, he gave it the name of the Baltimore Oriole.

"The Baltimore Oriole isn't a great musician, but he has a cheerful little song and call. Everybody likes him, and he is friendly too, and often nests quite near to people's houses.

"The Oriole builds a most unusual nest. (See nest on page 47.) That is, Lady Baltimore does. His lordship has nothing to do with it. While she is building their picturesque home, he does nothing much but fly around and sit and watch her and look gorgeous.

"But Lady Baltimore is a fine builder, and she doesn't hide her work in the crotch of a tree. She weaves a deep, basket-like nest and fastens it securely to the tip end of a branch. There it swings in the wind like a hanging pocket, twenty or thirty feet above the ground.

"She uses plant fibers and grass and any strings or little strips of cloth she can find. It is great fun to see her work.

"Perhaps, if you'd scatter a few bits of string or colored yarn around on the ground beside the big elm tree in the side yard, Lady Baltimore might weave them into her nest. Orioles usually come back to the same place, season after season, and there has been an Oriole family in that tree for several summers."

"I'll go, right now, and get some yarn from Aunt Molly," exclaimed Ann starting toward the door.

Then she stopped and came back, looking doubtfully at Uncle Jim.

"But if the Orioles come back to the same place, won't they live in the same house they had last year?"

"Oh, no. They like to come to the same tree, but they always build a brand new house every year. So they'll be glad to have some new building material.

"We like to have them nest near the house, too, because they eat wasps and spiders and grasshoppers and those bad tent-caterpillars. And if, once in a while, an Oriole likes a ripening grape for dessert we don't mind. He won't take the grapes unless the grapevine runs up into the tree where he can eat unseen. If we keep the grape vines trimmed back, the Orioles will leave them alone.

"Now you can run along and get your colored yarn. Maybe you'll see it, later on, woven into an Oriole's nest.... But, wait a minute...!"

Uncle Jim was looking at something outside the open window.

"Here's something that I want you to see. Look! Right out there in front of the petunias in Aunt Molly's window box.... A Ruby-throated Hummingbird!"

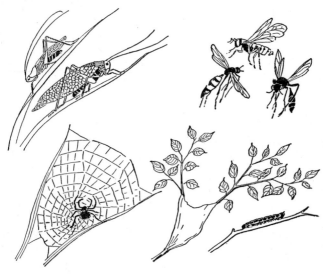

*Food of the Oriole*

| | |
|---|---|
| *Grasshoppers* | *Wasps* |
| *Spiders* | *Tent Caterpillar* |

# A Jewel With Wings

ANN moved quietly over toward the window and saw a tiny, brilliant bird hovering in front of the petunias, thrusting his long, slender bill deep down into each of the blossoms.

"You don't need to move so carefully," said Uncle Jim. "A Hummingbird isn't timid like a Cardinal. He won't be afraid of you. He's very small but he has a lot of spirit, and a temper that you wouldn't expect to find in so small a bird. He doesn't hesitate to fight a bird five times bigger than himself. And what is more he wins his fights. He is so small and so fast, and he goes into action so quickly that he's like a little arrow shooting through the air.

51

"He's pretty quarrelsome, too. He tries to keep all other Hummingbirds away from any of the flowers he has chosen for his own use.

"If another Hummingbird should come near, and the first Hummingbird should see him — Bing! There'd be a quarrel right away."

Ann stood looking at the exquisite little creature with its ruby-colored throat. It gleamed and flashed like a real jewel. As it moved about in the sunlight, it changed color from ruby red to a dull gold that shone like metal and then to an emerald green color.

"Oh!" she whispered. "He doesn't look real. He's so beautiful — so little, and so shiny. He looks as if he had a light inside him somewhere. And how can he stay up in the air in front of the flowers, like that?"

"His wings keep him up. Notice how they whir with that little humming sound that gives him his name. They move so fast you can hardly see them. They make a sort of blur around him. A Hummingbird makes between fifty and sixty wing strokes a second when he hovers in one place, and he makes about seventy-five wing strokes each second when he is flying.

"Hummingbirds don't light on their feet when they are taking nectar from a flower. They just hover in front of the blossom, dipping their needle-like bills into the nectar to take what they want. They never drink twice from the same blossom, either.

"I saw a Hummingbird, one day, thrust his bill into a honeysuckle blossom that was about ready to fall. As he touched the blossom, it came off and hung around his bill, covering his face like a mask. He was pretty cross about it, too. He jerked back and flung off the blossom, looking as if he thought someone had done it on purpose, and he'd like to know who it was!

"Oh! Oh! Now he's through with that flower.... There he goes off like a dart. And hear him squeak! He must have been annoyed by something. That's the way he sounds when he is angry."

"Is he going to find some more flowers to drink from?" asked Ann.

"Perhaps. But I think he's probably after some small insect, this time. He eats those, too, for a change.

"I'd like to have you see a Hummingbird's

nest. It is not much bigger than a walnut. And the eggs — there are always two of them — look like little white beans. When the eggs hatch, the babies look more like little black bugs than like little birds. You'd never dream they could become such lovely birds.

"But Father Hummingbird isn't interested in his children at all. He doesn't like family cares. As soon as Mother Hummingbird starts house-keeping, he is off and away.

"Someone has said that he knows if he stays near the nest, his brilliant plumage will show his enemies where the babies are, and so he flies away. I don't know how true this may be, but anyhow, he goes away and that's the last his family sees of him."

# Uncle Jim's Tame Crow

DOES anybody want to go with me?"

The sound of Uncle Jim's voice came up the stairway to Ann's ears as she was trying to make up her mind whether she wanted to wake up for good or lie in bed for a few sleepy minutes more.

In an instant she was wide awake. She sat up in bed.

"Go where?" she called.

"Bird hunting," said Uncle Jim, "but bird hunting with a field glass, not with a gun."

"I want to go." Ann scrambled out of bed and began dressing as fast as she could put her clothes on.

"Well, hurry up then. Wear an old pair of shoes and a dark dress. We'll go down through the field to the mill brook."

A half hour later, Ann, with a cooky in her hand, was ready to start.

Uncle Jim was waiting for her. He had on a dark shirt and suit, and he carried a field glass hanging from a leather strap over his shoulder.

"You're dressed just right," he said looking at Ann's brown dress. "And if you can eat the rest of that cooky on the way, we'd better start before the sun gets too high."

"Why did you tell me to wear a dark dress?" asked Ann. "Were you afraid I'd get it dirty?"

"No, that wasn't the reason. I don't want you to frighten the birds away. Birds, you know, are afraid of things that move, and they can see a light color moving toward them a great deal quicker than they can see something dull or dark. We want to get as near them as we can."

The day was warm, and the sun was bright, and Ann had a feeling of adventure as they set off across the wide meadow.

"What are we going to see?" she asked, skipping along by Uncle Jim's side.

"I don't know," he answered. "But something interesting. That, for one thing." He pointed toward the sky as the harsh *caw, caw* of a big black Crow, sailing over their heads, came floating down to them.

"That's only a Crow," said Ann. "I don't think he's very pretty."

"No, not especially pretty, but he's very smart. Farmers don't like Crows, and it's true that they do eat the farmers' corn. But they are remarkably clever about it. When they are feeding in a cornfield, they know enough to have one Crow keep watch to warn them of any danger.

"The Crow is a wise bird. He knows what a gun means, and if he sees anybody coming with a gun he sounds a shrill warning, and the Crows all take themselves off in a hurry.

"When I was a boy my brother and I had a tame Crow for a pet. The mother bird had been killed, and we thought we'd see if she had left any young ones.

"We climbed the tree where the old bird had her nest. It was quite a climb, too, because Crows always make their nests as high up as possible in tall trees.

"Well, we found a young Crow, all feathered out and nearly ready to leave the nest. We decided to take him home.

"But it was a problem to get him safely to the ground. We managed it though. We got an old umbrella and I carried it up the tree. When I reached the nest I tied a long piece of string to

the handle. Then I opened it and put the young Crow carefully inside, and lowered the open umbrella with its passenger down to my brother on the ground.

"We took the Crow home and made him a sort of nest in a basket and fed him some bread soaked in water. He liked it.

"In a few days he was able to hop out of his basket, and before long he was all over the place. He grew very tame. He never tried to fly away. He didn't fly much anyhow, just over the fence or up on a tree, that was all. He felt that the farm was his home.

"He was friendly with us all. He liked to be talked to and petted. We thought everything of that Crow. I guess we spoiled him, and he *was* mischievous.

"In those days we had to pump all the water we used in the house, and we always kept a pail of fresh drinking water in the kitchen. The Crow knew he wasn't to touch that drinking water — there was plenty outside for him to drink and take a bath in. But he had his own ideas about what he wanted. He'd watch, and when he saw a chance — splash! In he'd go to take

59

his bath in the drinking water, spoiling the water for everybody, and spattering the whole kitchen with his wet, flapping wings.

"He was always hiding bits of food or scraps of anything bright-colored. He'd take food from the chickens, and if he didn't want to eat it at the moment he'd hide it, sometimes under only a few straws. The chickens would usually find it again, so they were none the worse off. He'd even steal from the cat. He wasn't afraid of anything.

"The bantam rooster had a grudge against him and used to have a go at him every now and then. The Crow couldn't stand up and fight the rooster, but he knew a better way. He'd drop down and turn over on his back and fight the rooster with claws and beak, all at the same time. The bantam rooster would give right up. He couldn't handle that sort of fight.

"That Crow could mimic sounds so closely that he used to fool us. He would get into the cellar under the dining room and would mimic our voices when we were at the table. He couldn't say words, of course, but he'd copy sounds so perfectly that at first we were sure there was someone hiding in the cellar. We hunted and hunted, and then we found it was the Crow, just having a good time by himself."

"What fun you used to have when you were a little boy!" exclaimed Ann.

Then a sudden idea came to her.

"Why couldn't we have a tame Crow this summer, Uncle Jim? Oh let's!"

"Well now, I don't know." Uncle Jim looked thoughtful. "That's something that you'd have to talk over with Aunt Molly."

He smiled at her.

"But let's go and see some more birds, now," he said.

# A Lazy Bird

THE two bird hunters took a short cut to the brook across one end of a wide field. At the other end of the field several cows were grazing, with their noses close to the ground. Around the feet of the cows there were about ten or a dozen birds, some of them a dark brown and black, and some a dull gray.

Uncle Jim stopped and slipped the field glass from its leather case.

"Here," he said, handing it to Ann. "Look through this field glass. There's something over there that you should see. Look at those birds around the cows."

Ann had used the field glass before and knew just how to focus the lenses so that she could see the birds clearly. The glass magnified them so much that they seemed to be right at her feet. Some of them were hopping around in front of the cows' noses and some of them were right underneath the big animals.

"I should think," she said after she had looked for several minutes, "that they'd be afraid of those big cows. But they don't seem to be, a bit."

She handed the field glass back to Uncle Jim.

"What kind of birds are they?" she asked.

"They're Cowbirds. The reason they have that name is because they like to stay around where cows are feeding. The cows, when they are grazing, stir up swarms of flies and insects from the grass, and there they are, all ready for the Cowbird to eat without the trouble of hunting for them himself. But Cowbirds don't stay in the pasture with the cows all the time. They can be seen in many other places.

"The Cowbird, I am sorry to say, is not a very good citizen among birds. He is a shiftless creature, and the lady Cowbird is worse. A Cowbird won't build a nest for itself and it won't take care of its children, either.

"When the female Cowbird (she's the gray one) wants to lay an egg, she hunts around till she finds some smaller bird's nest, with one or two freshly laid eggs in it. Then as soon as she sees the other bird leave her nest for food, she slips in, and lays an egg, and flies away, leaving to the other bird the work of hatching and bringing up her children.

"As the Cowbird's egg is usually larger than the other eggs, it gets more warmth and hatches sooner; and the young Cowbird, having an earlier start, gets most of the food. It takes the middle of the nest and crowds out or pushes out the other little birds.

"The foster mother takes care of the greedy young Cowbird as if it were her own, and goes on feeding it till it is a great deal larger than she is herself.

"When we were talking about the Thrush cousins the other day, do you remember that I said I knew a story about a Veery?"

"You said it was a sad story," said Ann.

"Yes, it is. And it is a Cowbird story, too.

"One spring when I was a boy and didn't know as much about birds as I do now, I discovered a Veery sitting on her nest in a thicket of shrubs. A Veery is a shy bird, and I didn't want to frighten her. So I stood as still as I could and watched her. She was such a pretty bright-eyed little thing.

"After a while she left her nest, and I crept up to it and looked in. There was one light blue egg in the nest, lying beside two creamy white eggs speckled with brown.

"'A Cowbird's egg!' I said to myself. 'Isn't it lucky that I'm here to help the Veery.'

"Very carefully I slipped the single blue egg out of the nest and threw it away, and then before the Veery came back, I went home feeling that I had done something very fine in ridding the Veery's nest of the Cowbird's egg.

"A little later I looked in my bird book, and this is where the sad part comes in. I found that in my eagerness to help the Veery, I had thrown out the wrong egg, her own child, and I had left two Cowbird's eggs in the nest!"

"Oh, Uncle Jim, how dreadful!"

"Yes, wasn't it! But, you see, I thought that one blue egg was the Cowbird's. I ought to have known that a Veery's egg was blue, something like the eggs of a Robin.

"But, after all, maybe I saved the baby Veery a lot of hardship, for with two hungry baby Cowbirds in the nest it would have had no chance at all.

"And there's one thing certain. I have never, since that day, forgotten that the Cowbird lays a speckled egg."

# These Birds Harm Other Birds

THE Purple Grackle isn't very well liked either, by the other birds. You can often see several different kinds of birds unite in trying to drive him away. And you can be pretty sure when a lot of different birds agree in disliking one kind of bird, that there is a reason for it. The reason why the birds dislike the Grackle is that he robs their nests.

"He is a handsome black bird with a gleaming purplish, greenish, or bronzy metallic sheen on his feathers when the sun shines on him. You must have seen Grackles in the city parks, where numbers of them strut around on the smooth, grass lawns making quite a fine appearance.

"But with all the Grackle's good looks, he has a mean eye, pale yellow in color, and hard in its expression.

"And he has a dreadfully harsh, squeaky voice. He thinks he can sing, and he tries to do so. But when you hear what, in his opinion, is a song, you can't help thinking that he's made a big mistake. He sings about as well as I do."

Uncle Jim opened his mouth and began making groaning noises that sounded as if something were hurting him somewhere.

"Oh, Oh!" Ann put her hands over her ears. "Oh, Uncle Jim, please stop. You sound as if you were doing something terrible to your throat."

He stopped and grinned at her.

"Pretty bad, wasn't it?" he said. "Well, the difference between me and a Grackle is that *I* know I can't sing.

"And now I'll tell you about another bird that his neighbor birds don't like. He is the Starling, and the other birds don't like him because he is so terribly selfish. When the birds are hunting places to nest in the springtime, the Starlings try to snatch away all the best nesting places from the other birds, or drive them out after they have begun to build. Starlings especially like nesting places in holes in trees or in birdhouses. If there are any Starlings around, no other bird that has these choice building sites can enjoy any peace until after the Starlings have what they want.

"If the owner of a good nesting place will give it up to a Starling who wants it, the Starling won't bother the bird any more. But if the owner refuses to leave, then the Starling will fight.

"The Starling doesn't really belong here in America, anyway. In the year 1890 the first Starlings were brought over from Europe and let loose in Central Park, New York City. Before that time there hadn't been any Starlings in America.

"But they took so kindly to their adopted country and they have increased so rapidly in numbers that now there are quantities of them everywhere, in cities as well as in the country.

"The Starling is a glossy black bird with feathers tipped with buff or white, making little triangular specks all over his body. He has a long, sharp, yellow bill which he uses very fiercely when he is fighting. And you can always tell a Starling when you see him, because his tail is so short that he doesn't look quite complete.

"He is smart, too. Sometimes he will drive out a bird that is larger and stronger than he is himself, like the Flicker.

"I knew of a Starling that wanted a Flicker's place in the top of a dead tree, and the Starling was pretty clever about getting it, too. He watched, but he didn't interfere, while the Flicker dug out and shaped a hole for its nest in the tree. When the hole was nearly ready the Flicker turned its back for a moment, and then, in slipped the Starling and took possession.

"The Flicker, however, wasn't going to give up its house without a struggle. It put up a fight and did manage to get the Starling out of the hole. But — and this shows how clever the Starling was — though he had been beaten, he kept right on fighting outside the hole and he took up the Flicker's attention so that another Starling could slip into the hole and defend it against the Flicker.

"That meant that the poor Flicker had to fight again. In the end it had to give up the nest to the Starlings.

"If there were only a few Starlings, it wouldn't

matter so much, but there are a great many of them now, and they are beginning to crowd out some of our loveliest native birds."

"If I'd been there," declared Ann, "I'd have driven off the Starlings and let the Flicker keep its nest."

Starling

Flicker

"You'd probably have frightened off the Flicker, too," said Uncle Jim. "You haven't seen a Flicker yet, have you? Well just beyond this fence we'll be in the woods. We'll find some place near by where we can sit down, and then we'll see what we shall see. Maybe there will be a Flicker somewhere around."

They had reached the end of the field, which was fenced off from the woodland beyond. Uncle Jim let down the bars of the fence gate so they could go through, and then he put them up again so that the cows couldn't follow.

There were some tall trees close to the field, where they could sit in the shade and still be near enough to the brook to catch sight of any birds in the shrubbery on the bank of the stream.

"This is a good place to stop," said Uncle Jim. "We can sit here quietly on the grass, and while we're watching for a bird I'll tell you something about the English Sparrow. For he, too, like the Starling was brought over to this country from across the ocean. I guess everybody wishes he had stayed where he belonged.

"You see the English Sparrow everywhere. He is a little, dull-colored bird, brown, streaked with black above, and grayish white underneath. He is a tough little creature, staying in the North all winter, in the city or the country, and raising two or three families every year.

72

"He eats seeds and almost anything he can find. Sometimes he eats insect pests, and that is the only good thing I can say about him. For, like the rat among animals, the English Sparrow is like a cruel flying rat among the birds. He is sly and destructive. He is dirty and quarrelsome. And worse than anything else, he fights and drives away small, native song birds.

"He steals other birds' homes, especially those little birdhouses which have been put up for the song birds by their human friends. And he kills the young birds.

"The reason why we have so few Bluebirds around here nowadays is because the English Sparrows have stolen so many of their homes and driven them away."

*Female and Male*
*English Sparrows*

*Female Flicker*

*Male Flicker*

## Outwitting the Cowbird

UNCLE JIM talked in a low voice and sat very still so that the birds would not be afraid to come near. Ann, on the grass beside him, sat still, too.

Suddenly from one of the taller trees a rather large brown and black bird with a patch of bright scarlet on the back of its head flew down to the ground. It lit only a few feet in front of them, and began looking for insects in the grass.

"There he is!" whispered Uncle Jim. "A

74

Flicker. I hoped he'd show himself to us. A Flicker is one of the Woodpecker family, but he's a little different from his Woodpecker cousins because he doesn't peck into the trees for so much of his food as they do. He finds a good deal of his food on the ground. He likes ants and eats all he can get of them.

"The farmer likes the Flicker because he destroys grasshoppers, and the birds like him, too, because he is such a friendly neighbor to them."

"He has a mustache on his face," giggled Ann. "I mean that long black mark on his cheek. It makes him look sort of funny, doesn't it?"

"Oh, he likes that 'mustache.' That is the only mark that shows he is the head of the family. The lady Flicker is just like him in her markings, except that she doesn't have that black mustache, and so he values it very highly.

"He likes to show off before a lady Flicker, and when he is courting he will drum on a fence post or dead, hardwood tree to make a noise and attract his lady's attention."

The Flicker paid no attention to their talking. He hopped a little nearer and picked up an insect near Ann's feet. All of a sudden Uncle Jim broke into a little laugh. This startled the Flicker so that he spread his wings and flew away, showing a big white spot on his back as he did so.

"Oh Uncle Jim, why did you do that?" cried Ann. "Look, you've scared him away. What were you laughing at?"

"He was about ready to go anyway," said Uncle Jim. "And I laughed because I remembered a funny thing I once saw a Flicker do.

"I was down behind the barn, one day, and I noticed an old, rusty automobile fender which someone had dumped there. I was looking at it when along came a Flicker and lit on the fender.

"He may have taken the fender for a dead log. I don't know. At any rate, after a minute he began to drum on this old rusty fender. From the metal fender came a sound that he didn't expect at all.

"Well! ... It was the funniest thing to see that Flicker. He didn't realize that the fender was responsible for any of that lovely noise. He gave himself full credit for it all. He puffed out his chest and looked around him all swelled up with pride as if to say, 'Just see what I can do!' And then he tried it again — so satisfied with himself.

"To drum on a fence post or a tree makes a dull noise.  But this — well, he was a proud bird at the results!"

"Did the lady Flicker like the noise, too?"

"I don't know.  But she probably did.  There was a large family of young Flickers around here that summer."

While they had been talking, Uncle Jim had been watching a willow tree beside the brook. Now he reached for his field glass.

"Look over at that willow, Ann," he told her. "And I think you'll see a Yellow Warbler in a moment.  One just flew in among the branches. Probably his mate is nesting there.  He won't stay long.  All Warblers are restless, active birds darting in and out, and here and there.  He will. . . . Oh, there he goes! . . . Did you see him?"

"Was he a little yellow bird with brown on him?"

"Yes, his back is a sort of olive color, and he has some little chestnut colored streaks on his chest and sides.  He's as cheerful and gay in disposition as he is in color, and everybody likes him.

"The female is duller in coloring, but not in any other way.  She is, perhaps, the only bird

77

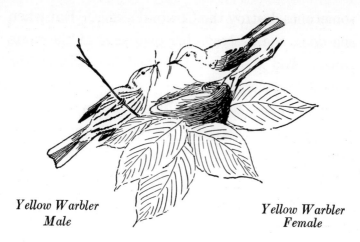

*Yellow Warbler*
*Male*

*Yellow Warbler*
*Female*

clever enough to outwit the Cowbird, when that lazy creature lays an egg in her nest.

"When the Cowbird tries to play this trick on the Yellow Warbler, the Yellow Warbler just calmly builds a second floor over the Cowbird's egg, and lays her own eggs on this new nest floor. She really makes her nest a two-story house, and the Cowbird's egg, walled off like this, can't hatch. Sometimes she even has to build a three-story house. But she won't hatch the Cowbird's egg, if she can help it.

"I don't know why the Yellow Warbler is so much smarter in this way than the other birds, but she is.

"The mother Yellow-breasted Chat, too, will

sometimes destroy the Cowbird's eggs. But when she does, she destroys her own eggs at the same time. And she doesn't rebuild her nest as the Yellow Warbler does.

"The Yellow-breasted Chat is the largest of the Warbler family. Like his cousin the Yellow Warbler, he has a yellow breast, but he has no chestnut colored streaks on his chest and sides, and he is much larger than the Yellow Warbler. He is about seven and one half inches long and the Yellow Warbler is only four and three quarter inches long.

"The Yellow-breasted Chat is really a funny bird — a sort of clown in the bird world, and he seems to enjoy a joke. Sometimes when he is flying, he will dangle his legs at their full length and let his head hang down, and he'll get himself into such odd positions that you would think he was really trying to make himself as funny as possible. He jerks his tail up and down a good deal when he's flying and this gives him a comical look.

"But he's shy and hard to see plainly if he thinks you are trying to spy on him. I spent more than an hour one morning trying to get a good look at a Chat on a tree in the ravine. He would always keep just on the opposite side of the tree from me, as if he were trying to hide from me. If I went around one way he would go the other way — just hiding.

"But when I gave it up at last, and sat down, he came out in plain sight and cocked his head and flapped his tail as if he were laughing at me."

*Yellow-breasted Chat*

*Blackburnian Warbler*

# The Big Warbler Family

THERE ought to be some more Warblers among these trees and shrubs," said Uncle Jim, looking around him.

"This is a good place for them. Let's see how sharp your eyes are, and which one of us can spot a bird first."

"Let's," agreed Ann with enthusiasm. "It won't matter what kind of bird it is, will it?"

"Not a bit."

They both watched closely, but Ann was the first to discover a bird.

"There's one!" she cried, pointing. "High up in that tree.... See! A lovely black and orange bird. Now he's gone again. But I saw him."

"Yes, I saw him too," said Uncle Jim. "That was a Blackburnian Warbler. He's a quick mover and one of the most brilliant of all the Warblers.

"He was named for an English lady, a Mrs. Blackburn. The name wasn't meant to tell what he looked like at all. But it so happens that it does describe him quite well.

"Some of the Blackburnian Warbler's feathers are as *black* as coal, and some are a vivid orange color, so bright that they seem almost to *burn* like a flame."

"I think it's a splendid name," declared Ann, "because it's such a good way to remember what he looks like — coal black and burning flame. I wish he would come back and let me look at him again."

"He doesn't stay long in any one place," said Uncle Jim. "But he may come back. Perhaps you can find him if you look through the field glass."

Ann took the field glass and looked through it,

but the Blackburnian Warbler was nowhere in sight.

"I can see another bird, though," she cried suddenly. "Oh! . . . he's gone. He was such a pretty one, but he flew away too quickly."

"I saw him, Ann. He was a Redstart. You can remember him by his name, too. It describes those yellowish red feathers in his beautiful tail. *Start*, or rather, *stert* is an old word meaning tail.

*Redstart*

"The Redstart is really gayer in color than the Blackburnian Warbler, and he's even quicker in his motions. The lady Redstart is not quite so bright a color as her mate but she is very pretty too, and just as quick. A Redstart is almost never still.  He doesn't stay up in the treetops as the Blackburnian Warbler does.  He hops about and flutters from twig to branch, and from limb to limb of shrubs as well as trees, hunting for insects.  Often he flashes out into space to snatch one from the air.

"The Redstart fairly dances his way through the forest.  He even keeps his tail partly outspread and his wings half open and quivering as he lights on a branch and trips along it to the end.  Perhaps he is proud of his handsome wings and tail marked with brilliant yellowish red against a glossy black.  At any rate he is always showing them.

"Many of the Warblers spend their winters in Mexico or in South America.  The people there have a different name for them.  The name they have is 'Candelita,' meaning little candle or torch, on account of the bright touches of orange or yellow that flame so brightly against the gray and olive and black of their plumage."

"Do all the Warblers have yellow or orange on them?" asked Ann.

"Oh, no.  Not all.  The Black and White Warbler — we talked about him before, you remember, hasn't any yellow. And the Black-throated Blue Warbler hasn't any, either. And there are some others. But so many of them do have yellow on them somewhere that the Mexican people like to think of them as little yellow candle flames."

*Black and White Warbler*

# More Warblers

THE Ovenbird is one member of the Warbler family that is so different from his relatives that you'd hardly think he belonged to them. His coloring is a dull, pale, olive gray. He has a crown of tawny brown outlined by two narrow black stripes, and he has a few black thrush-like stripes on his white breast. But he is much duller than any other Candelita.

"The Ovenbird has another marked difference, too. Most land birds hop when they are on the ground, or sometimes they run for a few steps. But the Ovenbird walks. There is something quite comical about the way he steps daintily along, placing one little pink foot primly in front of the other.

"He isn't the only bird that walks. Crows walk, and Grackles and Starlings and a few others. But most birds hop or run, and none of them walks with the neat dancing-school step of the Ovenbird.

"The Ovenbird's nest is different, too. It is built on the ground in the woods, and is covered with leaves and bits of bark. It is very cleverly hidden. There is an opening just large enough to let in the mother bird.

"The Ovenbird's nest isn't easy to find. If you do find one you'll notice that it is dome-shaped, a good deal like the old-fashioned, outdoor oven shown here.

"The shape of this nest is what gave the Oven-bird his name.

"Sometimes he is called the Teacher Bird, because he has a funny little song which sounds as if he were saying *Teacher, teacher, teacher.*"

Ann laughed out loud.

"Are you joking, Uncle Jim?   Does he really sound like that?"

"Well, somebody thought he did, and gave him that name.   You can listen to him and decide for yourself.

"The Yellow-throat is a Warbler that you'll always recognize after you've seen him once.   He

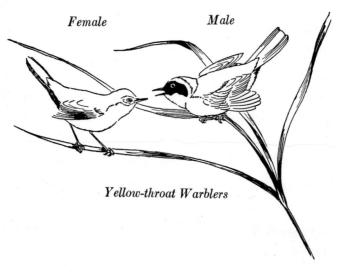

*Female*          *Male*

*Yellow-throat Warblers*

looks as if he were going to a fancy dress party, all dressed up in a smart yellow waistcoat, and wearing a little black velvet mask outlined in white, that he has put on to hide his face. The effect of the mask is very striking. You can't help but notice it.

"Maybe we'll see a Yellow-throat before we go home. The bushes beside the brook are just what he likes to dart around in, with his quick fidgety movements. He is one of the busiest and most useful of the Warbler family in the bug catching business.

"And he sings *witchety, witchety, witchety, WITCHETY!* his voice growing louder with every note. His song is quite a big sound for such a small bird.

"The lady Yellow-throat doesn't have a black mask. She doesn't really need one, for she wouldn't be going to a party anyhow. She has to stay at home to look after the children.

"There are a great many more warblers in this big family. There's the Pine Warbler that always nests in tall pine trees. There's the Chestnut-sided Warbler, with a broad band of rich chestnut color running along his sides. There's

89

*Chestnut-sided*

*Pine*

*Parula*

the bright Parula Warbler, and — oh, a lot of Warblers. You can look them up in the bird book at home.

"All the Warblers are rather timid and restless, and they are all very quick on the wing. I once saw a Magnolia Warbler catch a moth miller out of the air, and because he didn't like to eat the wings, he snipped them off with his bill. In so doing he accidentally dropped the moth.

"But he didn't lose it — Oh, no! With the swiftness of lightning, he swooped down upon the little moth and caught it up again before it could reach the ground. That meant pretty quick action.

"And all the Warblers eat millions and millions

of tiny insects which, if left to themselves, would destroy whole crops of peaches, plums, pears, and other fruit.

"Nearly all the time they are awake, these little birds are hunting for food, because just as an automobile when it is running needs plenty of gas, they need plenty of food fuel to keep them going. There isn't much food in one tiny gnat, you know. And so from early morning till dark these quick-moving Warblers keep catching and eating bugs and bugs and bugs and bugs — the very bugs that destroy the trees and the tree blossoms, and prevent many of the blossoms from ripening into fruit.

"The next apple that you eat may be a present to you from that Yellow Warbler that you saw in the willow tree down by the brook.

"And now I think we'd better go home. We've been away all morning. You've seen and heard enough about birds for one day, and there are many more days to come."

# Under the Bridge

IT rained for two whole days, and then the sun came out again.

Ann ran outdoors as soon as she had finished her breakfast, happy to be in the fresh, rain-washed air again. The grass looked greener, the flowers looked brighter, and the sky was clear and blue.

She saw Uncle Jim backing the car out of the garage, and in a twinkling she was there beside him.

"Are you going to the village, Uncle Jim?" she called, running along beside the car. "Oh, please take me with you!"

Uncle Jim stopped the car and opened the door.

"All right, hop in," he said, holding the door open with one hand. "I was going to call you, anyway, if I didn't find you around outside the house. There's something on the way to the village that I'd like to show you."

They drove along for nearly a mile, and then they came to a little bridge over a small gully.

Uncle Jim pulled up at the side of the road and stopped the car.

"This is where we get out," he said. "We're going to climb down part way into that little gully. I saw a Phoebe fly under this bridge, the other day when I was coming back from town. I shouldn't wonder if she was a mother Phoebe with a nest down under here somewhere."

Uncle Jim and Ann climbed down the steep side of the gully far enough to see under the bridge. And when they looked, sure enough, there was a Phoebe's nest built on a beam right underneath the bridge. The mother Phoebe, a brownish gray

bird with a yellowy white breast, was sitting on the nest.

She was watching them closely to see that they didn't come too near, but she didn't seem to be afraid of them.

"She's very gentle and friendly," said Uncle Jim in a low voice. "I think she likes people, if they don't come too close, or move too fast to frighten her.

"Notice the tip end of her bill. See how the point is bent down sharply. That is one mark of the Flycatcher family, and the Phoebe is a Flycatcher. She likes to perch on a dead limb or a fence post, and from there she will dart out like a flash and snap an insect right out of the air. Sometimes you can hear the sharp little snap of her bill as she catches a bug.

"Then she will come back to her post again and switch her tail sideways, like a friendly dog wagging its tail when it is pleased. The Phoebe is a very nice bird, and a very useful one, too."

"I wish she'd fly away so we could see her eggs," said Ann.

"Oh, no. We don't want to frighten or disturb her, not when she's so gentle and trusting.

I think we'd better go away ourselves and leave her alone now."

They said good-by to the Phoebe and started to climb back to the road again.

"I should think she'd be scared by the noise cars make going over the bridge, almost on top of her," said Ann, scrambling up the steep side of the gully.

Uncle Jim had already reached the road. He turned around and gave his hand to Ann.

"She doesn't seem to mind, at all," he said, pulling the little girl up beside him. "I guess she's learned that she is pretty safe right where she is."

"You said there was a Flycatcher family, Uncle Jim," said Ann as she stopped to catch her breath. "Are there as many Flycatcher cousins as there are in the Warbler family?"

"No, the Flycatchers don't seem to have quite so many relatives as the Warblers, but they are a very important family, just the same. They are duller in coloring than most of the Warbler family. They are a little chunkier in build, too, and their bills are bent sharply downward at the tip end.

"They live very largely on flying insects which they snap out of the air with surprising skill. They hardly ever miss a bug when they dart out after one, no matter how good a dodger the bug may be."

While Uncle Jim and Ann had been talking, they had come up to the car. Uncle Jim unlocked the door.

"We'll have to be moving along," he said, "or I'll never get my errands done in town. We can talk as we go. In with you."

He jumped in after Ann and started the car. "I'll tell you about the Kingbird," he said.

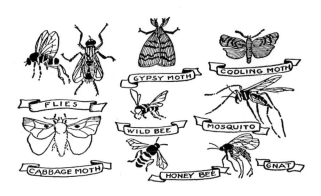

*Flycatchers live largely on flying insects.*

## Flycatcher Habits

THE Kingbird can be called the king of the Flycatcher family. He is quite fearless in attacking his enemies, and though he's only about nine inches long he isn't afraid to attack birds, like the Hawk or the Crow, that are a good deal larger than he is.

"He will dash at these birds with a sort of screaming battle cry, which he keeps up all the time he is fighting them. Sometimes he will even light on his enemy's back, and do all the damage he can there.

"But he isn't a quarrelsome bird, generally. He fights only those birds that might harm him, or those that loaf around his house, or pay too much attention to his mate. Any bird with any pride at all would do that. Wouldn't he?"

"Of course," laughed Ann.

"The Kingbird's coloring is mostly black and gray with a white breast, and a white-tipped tail. But he has one kingly mark that helps you to know him. It is a little bit of orange-red right on the top of his head.

"He gets his living out of the air too. He eats mosquitoes, as many as he can find, along with other insects. He ought to have a lot of credit for that, don't you think?"

"Oh my, yes!" exclaimed Ann, starting to scratch as she remembered a number of mosquito bites that had been troubling her. "Can't we get some Kingbirds to come and live in our yard?"

"Maybe you can if you scatter some food for them," said Uncle Jim hopefully.

"And now here's a story about two Kingbirds, that in spite of their superior fighting qualities, did not win in a fight.

"I once saw a gentle little Phoebe get the best of not one but two Kingbirds, and each Kingbird was a whole inch bigger than the Phoebe.

"I was fishing, one day, sitting on the bank of the old mill stream. On the dead limb of a tree hanging over the stream, there was a Phoebe. It was a grand place for the Phoebe to catch little bugs and flies, and two Kingbirds flying by got that idea too.

"They settled on the branch and requested the Phoebe to move on. But the Phoebe said, 'I'll do nothing of the sort. I was here first, it's my place.'

"The Kingbirds rather insisted. The Phoebe lost her temper, and so did the Kingbirds. I think perhaps the Kingbirds may have been just young birds, more blusterers than real fighters. But at any rate they came off very much second best, and the Phoebe was left in possession of the place. They knew they were conquered and they gave up.

"Probably the Phoebe was so much quicker on the wing, being small, that she could get under motion quicker, and get away from the Kingbirds. She could dodge in and get a few feathers and then get away. It was a surprising fight, though, and I felt like cheering the Phoebe for holding her own."

Uncle Jim stopped talking while he drove past a heavy, lumbering truck; then he went on telling about the other birds of the Flycatcher family.

"The Crested Flycatcher looks a little like the Kingbird, only his tail is a reddish brown and he doesn't have the Kingbird's orange-red patch on his head. Instead he has a little crest.

"Like the rest of his cousins he is a skillful bug catcher, but unlike any of his relatives he has one very curious habit — the Crested Flycatcher always builds into his, or rather her nest, a part or all of a cast-off snake skin."

"Snakes, Uncle Jim? I thought birds didn't like snakes."

"They don't. But this bird nearly always weaves a piece of snake skin into her nest. Nobody knows why. And no other bird does anything like this. The Crested Flycatcher is the only one to do it. So if you ever find a nest partly made of snake skin, you can be sure a Crested Flycatcher built it."

"How awfully queer! A snake's skin, ugh!" Ann shivered. "I'd like to find out why, wouldn't you?"

"Yes, I would, but I don't think we ever shall." Uncle Jim stopped the car at a main crossroad and waited while a number of cars went by.

"We're getting pretty close to town," he said, starting again, "but I'd like to tell you a little about two other members of this Flycatcher family before we get there.

"One of these Flycatchers is the Wood Pewee. He is something like his Phoebe cousin, but he is more timid and prefers to live in the woods farther away from people. He's about an inch smaller too. And it's rather odd, but in spite of his shyness the Pewee never seems to be afraid to let

anyone know where his nest is. As for Mother
Pewee, she will go right to her nest even when
she knows you are watching her.

"I was in the wood lot one day last summer
when I heard a Pewee making a great fuss about
something. I looked and found a young Pewee
that had fallen either from the nest or from the
branch, where it may have been perching. The
little bird was all feathered out and ready to leave
the nest, but it was pretty helpless on the ground.

"I picked up the poor baby, and it wasn't in
the least afraid of me. It cuddled right down in
my hand as if it were in a warm nest and closed
its eyes.

"The mother hopped about on the branch of

the tree and watched me closely, but she didn't seem to be very greatly worried, and I talked to her quietly and told her not to be afraid. Then I set the young bird on the branch and it seemed to be all right."

"What happened after you did that, Uncle Jim?"

"I don't know. I went away and left them together, and the next day they were gone. You see, the young bird was almost ready to fly when it fell.

"The Pewee has an odd, plaintive little call, which gives him his name. Sometimes he seems to be saying *Pee-a-wee*, and sometimes he seems just to be sighing *Dear me!* Like this" — and in a very small and almost questioning voice Uncle Jim brought out the words, *De-ar me!*

"Try it yourself — but not now — later on. We are almost in the village and I've just time to say a word about the Least Flycatcher.

"As you can tell by his name, the Least Flycatcher is the smallest one of the Flycatcher family — he's only about five inches long. But though he's smaller than his various relatives he is a good deal like them in looks and habits. He

104

is just as friendly as the Phoebe, and he is just
as good at catching flies.

"He has another name too. He's often called
the Chebec, and he tells you so himself very
clearly, jerking his head and tail every time he
says it, and he says it quite often, too, *Che-bec,
che-bec, che-bec!* ... But we can't talk about any
more Flycatchers because here we are at the post
office."

*Least Flycatcher*

*Meadowlark*

## Music in the Fields

ANN waited in the car while Uncle Jim went into the post office. But he wasn't gone long. He came out in a few minutes with several letters which he slipped into his coat pocket as he got into the car.

"Now for the grocery store," he said. "We have a good many things to get there for Aunt Molly."

He took a slip of paper from his pocket.

"Here's the list. You count them off on your fingers while I read them. Now listen: sugar, coffee, macaroni, oranges, crackers, soap, and a bottle of vinegar. Seven things. Do you think we can remember all of those?"

"Oh, yes," said Ann. "You can remember what they are and I'll remember that there are seven things."

She got out of the car at the store and wandered around looking at the things in the show cases while Uncle Jim talked with the storekeeper and did his shopping.

When he was ready to go he called her. All the packages were piled on the back seat except one — a bag of candy, which he dropped into Ann's lap.

"Because," said Uncle Jim, "I think, by this time, you must be feeling ready to eat again, like a young Robin." And he laughed as she thanked him, reaching eagerly for the bag.

"We're going home a different way," said Uncle Jim, turning off from the main highway to a dirt road. "I think if we take the meadow road we may see something interesting. We'll try it anyway."

Ann was enjoying her candy, and for a while they drove slowly along the quiet road.

Then, from somewhere above them there came a regular burst of lovely bird song. It rippled and twinkled. Each note bubbled out so rapidly that it seemed almost to fall right over the note ahead of it.

"A Bobolink," said Uncle Jim, and brought the car quietly to a stop.

"Where is he? I can't see him," said Ann looking all around her.

"Over there. He's coming down. See, he's lighting on that tall weed stalk. He is a black and white bird, with a big buff patch on the back of his neck."

"I see him now." Ann leaned her head out of the car window to listen. "What a lovely song he has!"

"Yes, that's the Bobolink, one of our best bird musicians. There is probably a Bobolink nest near here. Bobolinks always nest on the ground.

"Mr. Bobolink is a useful bird, as well as a fine singer. That is, he is useful in his northern home, because he eats grasshoppers and other bugs and no end of harmful weed seeds.

"But in the southern rice fields, he behaves very differently. Down there he is quite a pest, and people don't like him. They call him the 'Rice-bird' or the 'Reed-bird.'

"Bobolinks leave for the South early in the fall, and reach the southern rice fields as the rice crop is ripening. They do great damage there, for Mr. and Mrs. Bobolink and the whole family eat so much rice they grow as fat as butter balls.

"And because they do this they bring down punishment upon themselves. After they have grown nice and fat on this rice diet, they are hunted as game birds, and many of them are shot and eaten. 'Reed-birds on toast' is considered quite a tasty dish in the South."

"It seems too bad to shoot them," said Ann. "I don't suppose they know how bad they are to eat the rice."

"No, I don't suppose they do. But the farmers can't afford to lose their rice crops, either, you know."

"That's so," agreed Ann, and thought it over for a few minutes.

Suddenly she turned her head to listen. A snatch of bird song sounded from the meadow.

"Is that the Bobolink singing again?" she asked.

"No, that's a Meadowlark. He's a fine singer, too, but different. There he goes again. Listen! ... He sounds a good deal like a flute, doesn't he, so sweet and clear.

"The Meadowlark hasn't any bad habits. He is a real friend to the farmer, and should never be killed. His summer food is made up almost entirely of insects that destroy the farmer's crops. If there were more Meadowlarks there wouldn't be so many bugs.

"There he is ... in the grass, that short-tailed, brown bird streaked with black. See him? He has a yellow breast, too, and a black necktie.

"The Meadowlark is a fine singer. He is a real friend to the farmer and should never be killed."

And he is one of the few birds that, like the Oven-bird, walks, while other birds would hop or run.

"The Meadowlark builds his nest on the ground, the same as the Bobolink. But Meadow-larks hide their nests so skillfully that you'd have a hard time trying to find one."

"I'm glad we came this way," said Ann. "Did you know we'd find a Bobolink and a Meadow-lark here?"

"Not exactly. Of course this is a good place to find them, but I came this way because, a little farther along, there is a swamp beside the road. With all the rain we've been having, the swamp should be full of water, and I was thinking that perhaps we could see some Killdeer there."

*A Meadowlark builds its nest on the ground.*

## A Sentinel on Guard

KILLDEER, that's a funny name for a bird," said Ann. "It sounds as if they were awfully fierce birds. Are they?"

"No, not a bit. The name comes from their shrill cry, which sounds like *Kill-deer*, or *Kill-dee*. They are a little different from the birds that you have seen so far. They are what we call Shore Birds, because they like to live near the edge of the water.

"They are about ten and a half inches in length. Their legs are long enough for them to run around in the shallow water on the shore of the ocean, or at the edges of ponds and streams, where they can pick up grub worms.

"The Killdeer catches bugs and mosquitoes from the air, too. He can run quickly on his feet, but he is just as quick in his flying. Sometimes you can find him in plowed fields following the farmer's plow and feeding on the grubs and worms that have been turned up in the moist earth.

"When it comes to making a nest Mrs. Killdeer wastes very little energy. Just a small hollow on the ground somewhere near the water, and not too damp, is good enough for her house. She lays four eggs, creamy white ones spotted with brown. You'd be surprised to find how hard it is to see them because they look so much like the pebbles on the ground around them.

"When the eggs hatch, the babies come out of the shell already covered with down. They are not naked and skinny like the other baby birds we have been talking about. They are more like little chickens or ducks. They start right in running around and picking up bits of food.

"But the mother has to take care of them and show them where to find their food. She keeps them warm in the nest, too, under her wings, until they are big enough to look out for themselves.

"Mother Killdeer is very careful of her children, even though she isn't much of a housekeeper. If you drive her from her nest, or if you come too close, she will try all sorts of tricks to get you away.

"She will draw your attention from her nest by making you think you can catch her easily. She is so clever that she will run or flutter away just in front of you crying pitifully, and with one wing hanging down as if it were broken. Sometimes she will almost fall over, or gasp as if she couldn't go a bit farther.

"But she will keep just out of your reach, leading you farther and farther away from her nest until she thinks it is safe. Then with a mocking cry she will fly away."

"How does she know enough to do that, Uncle Jim?"

"Oh, it's her nature. She is a smart bird.

"I remember happening to find a Killdeer on her nest, late one afternoon. She was cuddling her babies under her wings. I stopped to watch

114

her, but I kept far enough away so that she wouldn't be frightened.

"And then I saw several Grackles come along.

"Mother Killdeer didn't like that. She knew just how mean Grackles could be. There were six or eight of them in the group, wandering around. If one of them came too close she would fly up and chase it away.

"But there were too many Grackles for her to handle and so, after a minute or two, she turned and ran for Father Killdeer to come and help her.

"Father Killdeer was hunting food not far away, but he stopped at once and came hurrying back with her.

"Mother Killdeer returned to her nest and gathered her babies under her wings again, and Father Killdeer started in to guard the place.

With his family in the center of a circle that was about ten feet across, he began walking around and around the circle.

"Whenever a Grackle would come too close, Father Killdeer would chase him away with harsh cries that sounded like, 'Out of my front yard, sir! And in a hurry too.'"

"Did the Grackles do as he told them?"

"Yes, they did, and very promptly, at that. He meant business and they knew it. He kept walking around and around till it was dark, and then I came away. He was still at it."

While Uncle Jim had been talking, they had been moving slowly along the road. Now they came to the pond.

"There it is," said Uncle Jim. "And look at all the Killdeer! There must be a hundred of them. Aren't they noisy things!"

"They sound sort of cross," said Ann, "and their legs *are* long, aren't they?" She put her head out of the car window to see better, and then drew it back. "It's pretty windy. I shouldn't think the birds would like it."

"They don't like it when the wind blows their feathers the wrong way. But when they are

116

flying they always land against the wind, like airplanes, so they won't tip over."

Uncle Jim and Ann sat watching the dull gray-ish brown birds for a little while, and then Uncle Jim started the engine of the car.

"I wish we could stay longer," he said. "But we ought to be going along. Aunt Molly will be wanting her groceries."

"All . . . right. . . ." Ann spoke the words slowly, looking back at the Killdeer. Then — "Oh, wait!" she cried. "Look!"

The birds were all standing like soldiers at attention, and all facing in the same direction as if they were waiting for some word of command.

117

Then suddenly, just as if one of them had said, "Let's go!" away they all flew. But not very far.

In a few minutes, back they came again and landed against the wind all looking straight ahead and standing perfectly still, as before, like a company of well-trained soldiers.

After a moment of this soldier-like attention they broke ranks — so to speak, and began to wander around as before.

"Well!" declared Uncle Jim. "That was worth waiting to see, wasn't it? It certainly looks as if they must have had a leader to give them orders."

"Oh," breathed Ann. "Oh, I'm glad we didn't miss it. But wasn't it queer!"

The car bumped over a rut in the road, and Uncle Jim grunted. Then he smiled at the eager little girl.

"You'll see a great many queer things, if you watch the birds," he said.

# A Hungry Heron

THE automobile turned in at the gate and came to a stop in the driveway.

Ann jumped out and Uncle Jim got out, too, and began to gather up the packages that were on the back seat. As he took them out he counted them. Suddenly he looked surprised.

"See here, Ann," he called. "Something's wrong. There are only six packages here, and there ought to be seven. We have forgotten something."

"There were seven things, Uncle Jim. I counted them before we started home."

Uncle Jim began to laugh. "You counted your bag of candy for one of them. That's what you did, and the candy was an extra."

He fumbled in his pocket. "Where's that list? What did we forget?" He pulled out the little piece of paper with the list of things he was to get. He looked at the list.

"The bottle of vinegar," he said, and looked solemnly at Ann. "We've been very bad. I guess this means we'll have to make another trip to the village."

Ann giggled and put her fingers over her mouth, as if she ought to feel guilty.

"Do we have to go right back, now?" she asked.

"I'll ask Aunt Molly." Uncle Jim picked up the groceries and took them into the house.

In a minute or so he came out again with a smile on his face.

"Aunt Molly says we won't have to go again today," he told Ann. "But we're not to go off anywhere else now, either, because dinner is almost ready."

He sat down on the porch and took off his hat.

"You know," he said, "between you and me, I rather hoped we would have to go back past that pond. There's been a big bird hanging around there lately — a Great Blue Heron. I'd like you to see him. I was going by there yesterday at just the right moment, and I had a chance to watch him for a little while.

"A Heron is *really* big. From the tip of his bill to the end of his tail he's about four feet long. His great blue-gray wings measure about six feet from tip to tip. His legs are long, too, very long, so that he can wade in the water and catch fish and frogs or whatever he can find to suit him.

"When you see him walking through shallow water, lifting each foot carefully above the surface of the water and sliding it in again, so gently that he scarcely causes a ripple, you can be sure he's after something. And it is too bad for any crawfish or frog that doesn't notice his approach.

"He's always hungry, but he never seems to get fat no matter how much he eats.

"Sometimes he just stands still in shallow water near some reeds, if there are any reeds around.

He stands as still as a statue, with his long slim neck doubled up into the shape of an S.  You might think he was asleep and dreaming, but he's wide awake.  His sharp eyes are searching the water all around him, and a Heron doesn't need any glasses to help him see.  He can see a great deal better than you or I can.

"When a fish comes within striking distance out shoots that long neck and — Whing! goes

that sharp bill.  He almost never misses his mark.

"In a second that fish is on its way down the Heron's throat, and he has become as still as a statue again.

"He catches insects, too, and that's what I saw him do yesterday.  He lighted on the ground not twenty feet from the car.  I had a perfect close-up of him.

"He was very cautious.  He didn't seem to know that I was in the car.  Maybe the sunlight on the windshield dazzled him.  At any rate he didn't notice me.  He seemed to feel pretty safe.

"He'd take one step and look around him, and then take another step and look — walking in a sort of sneaky way and reaching out with his great long neck at every step.

"All of a sudden a dragon fly flew past, and — like a flash, quicker than my eye could follow, he stretched out his jack-in-the-box neck and caught the dragon fly in his bill.

"Then he went through all the motions of chewing, just as if he were biting, or crunching the dragon fly. Only birds, you know, never chew. They have no teeth.

"After opening and shutting his bill a few times he spit out the dragon fly's wings. He didn't seem to like those long, scratchy things.

"Having got rid of the wings, he went on sneaking down toward the pond to get something more juicy from the water.

"I was sorry to see the Heron eat the dragon fly, because dragon flies eat mosquitoes and other troublesome insects. But I guess he felt that it was another bit of food and, as such, not to be overlooked. A Heron never likes to miss an opportunity to eat."

## Uncle Jim Can't Fool the Towhee

YOU know such a lot about birds, Uncle Jim," said Ann, watching him as he washed out the bird bath with a stream of water from the garden hose, and then filled it again with fresh water.

Uncle Jim turned off the water and began to wind up the hose.

"There's a great deal that I don't know," he said. "I've never made a really scientific study of birds, but I have had a good time watching them. I've noticed little things they do, and what they eat, and I've listened to them singing and calling to one another. That's really the best way to learn about birds and their habits, and it's fun. But it's a big help to have a good bird book too.

"I have seen all the things I've been telling you about, and hundreds of things besides. You have seen a good deal yourself, Ann, in just this one summer, by keeping your eyes and ears open.

"There's something to see right now." He pointed to the bird bath. "Look at that Red-eyed Vireo."

A grayish, olive-green bird, a little over six inches long, with reddish-brown eyes was splashing around for dear life in the bath. He was having what seemed to be a wonderful time spattering water all over everywhere.

When his bath was finished he hopped up on the rim of the bird bath, but on looking back decided that he must have another dip. So in he jumped again and made the water fly in all directions.

Once more he hopped up on the rim and shook himself ready to fly. Once more he seemed unable to tear himself away, so back he went for still another bath — just enjoying the water.

"Well!" exclaimed Uncle Jim. "Bath tubs

must have been scarce in his summer home, and drinking water, too."

"It's a funny name," said Ann, "Red-eyed Vireo."

"Look at his eyes. They distinguish him from the other members of his family. It's a good name for him. He's the Vireo you see most often, and hear most often, too. He keeps up an almost endless song. If there is a Red-eyed Vireo around you will know it, for he'll keep right on announcing his presence, stopping only a second or so at a time to snap up an insect.

"His song is a kind of sing-song. Because of this, and because, while he is singing, he hops around facing first in one way and then in another, something like a preacher talking to an audience, he has been called the 'Preacher Bird.'

"And the lazy Cowbird must think the lady Vireo is like a preacher's wife, who is supposed to take care of orphan children. Whether this is so or not, the Red-eyed Vireo's nest is one in which the Cowbird often leaves an egg or two."

Uncle Jim got up from the porch steps where he had been sitting and stretched his arms.

"I'm going down to the lower meadow for a

126

little while," he said. "Do you want to go along with me?"

Ann was on her feet in a second.

"Don't I always want to go with you?" she said, jumping up and down on the garden walk beside him.

"Nice girl!" Uncle Jim smiled and took her hand. "I'm going to miss you when the summer is over and you've gone home."

They went through the back garden gate and out into the field beyond. As Uncle Jim was closing the gate behind them, there was a scuffling, scratching sound among some leaves beside the path. A bird with a black head and back, and a brown and white breast and sides flew up from the ground with a call that sounded like *Chewink! Chewink! Chewink!*

"My goodness!" exclaimed Ann. "Look! He isn't even as big as a Robin. And I thought he was a chicken or a squirrel, making all that racket. What kind of bird is he?"

"He's a Towhee," answered Uncle Jim. "But we usually call him a Chewink on account of his call. It is one of his odd habits to scratch on the ground in that way. He uses first one foot and then the other, more like a chicken, really, than like most birds.

"He was after some kind of ground bug, or beetle. He does a good deal of rustling around among the leaves on the ground, scratching for his dinner.

"A Towhee, or Chewink, is a very helpful bird in this business of getting rid of bugs. He goes after them in the early spring, before the bugs have had a chance to start their large families. Bugs certainly do have enormous families! The death of one bug in the early spring is equal to the death of a whole swarm of bugs later in the summer.

"A mother Chewink usually builds her nest on the ground, though once in a while you may find one in a low bush. And it's a queer thing, but

"A Towhee, or Chewink, is another helpful bird
in this business of getting rid of harmful bugs."

neither the father nor mother Chewink seems to worry if you come close up to the nest, provided you don't disturb it.

"Most birds, you know, make a big fuss if anyone comes too close to their nests."

"But we wouldn't hurt them, Uncle Jim."

"Well, they don't know that, and you can't expect any bird to take chances with its young."

The Towhee had lighted on a branch of a tree beside the garden gate, and the sound of his *Chewink!* came crisply down to the two on the path below.

Uncle Jim looked up at the tree.

"I believe that bird knows me," he grinned. "And he hasn't much of an opinion of me, either. I was passing this way, yesterday, and I came upon him scratching on the ground, and calling *Chewink* as he scratched. I stopped to watch him. He'd scratch a little and then he'd say *Chewink*, and then scratch a little more and repeat *Chewink*, *Chewink*.

"I thought I'd try it, so I said *Chewink*, as nearly like his sound as I could make it. He stopped and looked at me and gave two or three very plain *Chewinks*.

"I said it again.   At that he gave a brisk little scratch at the ground and the *Chewinks* fairly bounced out of his throat.   They came faster and faster till at last he flew up and at me as if he were going to hit me.   But he went on right over my head, giving me a look of disgust as he passed.   It was his way of saying,

"'Trying to fool me, huh?   Well you'll have to try a whole lot harder than that — silly!'"

*Bobwhite*

# The Bobwhites Disappear

AS they talked they were walking along a crooked path across the field. Uncle Jim kept looking at the ground beside the path. He looked first on one side and then on the other, till Ann became quite curious.

"What are you looking for, there on the ground?" she asked him.

"I'm looking for Bobwhite," said Uncle Jim.

"Who's Bobwhite?"

"He's a Quail. There must be a Quail family right around here somewhere. I heard his cheerful call of *Bobwhite!* while we were watching the Red-eyed Vireo taking his bath. We'll see him,

131

I guess, if we watch. He likes to scratch around for seeds or grain on the ground in fields like this. But he certainly does know how to hide himself.

"Look for a chunky, roundish bird about ten inches long, speckled with different shades of brown and with black. He has a white throat too — or a buff throat, if it is Mrs. Bobwhite.

"Bobwhite is a friend of mine. I haven't let anyone around this field shoot at him all summer, though he makes very good eating. You've probably eaten quail yourself and liked it.

"There!" Uncle Jim pointed suddenly to the ground ahead of them. "There's Bobwhite now. Or, I guess it's Mrs. Bob. Don't go any nearer."

"Where is she? Where?" whispered Ann anxiously, looking in the direction to which he was pointing. "I can't see any bird at all."

"Right there, beside the path. It's Mrs. Bob, all right, and some of her children are with her. They're all keeping perfectly still. She's flattened herself out on the ground hoping we won't notice her, because she's very much the color of the earth and the dead grass around her. Her babies are, too. Can't you see her?"

"Oh, now I do," whispered Ann. "And her babies — aren't they cunning! They look like little pecan nuts with feet on them. How do they know enough to keep so still?"

"Just instinct. They know how to hide, almost from the minute they are hatched. They come out of the eggshell knowing how. Like the baby Killdeer, they are covered with soft down when they are hatched. As soon as they have kicked themselves free from their shells, and the down on their little bodies has dried, they begin to run around.

"Mrs. Bob makes her nest of grass and leaves, somewhere out of sight among tall grasses, when she can find a good place, or under a small bush,

or in the woods, or under a log. Whenever she leaves her nest before the eggs are hatched, she covers them over carefully with leaves. She lays from ten to eighteen eggs. Mrs. Bob raises a big family, and she is a good mother to them."

At that moment Mr. Bob, himself, rose suddenly with a sharp whirring sound of his wings from almost underneath Ann's feet, and startled her so that she gave a little squeal.

Uncle Jim laughed.

"That's a trick of his. It's a smart one, too, for it catches you off guard. And . . . look! Mrs. Bob and the babies seem to have melted right away. Aren't they smart at hiding themselves!"

"It seems to me," remarked Ann, "that a good many birds are pretty smart."

"They have to be smart, if they want to live," said Uncle Jim.

*Screech Owl*

# Too-Hoo, Hoo-Hoo!

ANN set down her glass of milk and looked soberly across the table at Uncle Jim.

"Do birds ever cry?" she asked him.

Uncle Jim was putting some sugar into his cup of coffee. He stirred it around slowly as if thinking.

"Why, yes," he said after a minute. "They do, in a way. A bird will make sharp cries of distress if an enemy attacks its nest. If a baby bird falls out of the nest, the parent birds make quite a good deal of fuss."

"That's not the sort of crying I mean. What I mean is, do they cry the way we do when we're sick or feeling bad about something? I'm sure I heard a bird crying last night."

Uncle Jim smiled. "Oh, now I know. What you heard was a Screech Owl."

Ann looked doubtful, as though she found this explanation hard to believe.

"Well . . . but he wasn't screeching," she protested. "He was crying."

"Yes, I know, but it was a Screech Owl you heard. I heard him too. That crying sound is his call. I don't know how he ever got such a name. He doesn't screech, he gives a mournful, trembling sort of little wail."

"Yes, that's just the way it sounded," agreed Ann. "What was the matter with him?"

"Nothing was the matter. That's just his natural call. He keeps still during the day, and it isn't until evening that he begins making those mournful sounds.

"In the South the Screech Owl is often called the Shivering Owl, because his shivering, mournful call after dark makes some people feel kind of shivery, too."

"Do you suppose the Screech Owl has a nest somewhere near here?" asked Ann.

"I don't know." Uncle Jim finished his cup of coffee, and leaned back in his chair. "I haven't seen one, but owls keep out of sight pretty well during the daytime. They build their nests usually in some hole in a tree or a stump. Quite often they use a deserted Woodpecker's nest, or an old hole dug out by a Flicker.

"It is after sundown that they come out and begin to hunt. They fly quietly through the air, hunting for mice, and rats, and toads, and lizards, and grasshoppers. Once in a while a big owl will catch a bird or a little chicken, but that is mostly when he can't find enough of something else.

"The Screech Owl is only about ten inches long. He has a funny face with big, round eyes. Most other birds have their eyes at the sides of their heads, but an Owl's eyes are in front and look straight ahead, the way ours do, so that he has to turn his head around to look on one side. There is a ring of feathers around his eyes which make a kind of frame for them. This gives him an amusing look of open-eyed surprise."

"Wouldn't it be a good idea," suggested Ann, coming around the table to Uncle Jim's chair, "for us to go and see if we could find a Screech Owl's nest?"

Uncle Jim looked at her with a smile in his eyes.

"You think that would be a good idea? Well, maybe. But we might have to hunt for a long, long time. An Owl's nest is very hard to find."

He put his arm around her and drew her closer to his side.

"I think it would be a better idea for me to tell you about another Owl, a big one, that you're likely to hear any night after dark, calling, '*Oot-too-hoo, hoo-hoo!*'

"Some people call him the Hoot Owl, but there

*Great Horned Owl*

are other owls that hoot.  This one's real name
is the Great Horned Owl."

"Horns on an owl!  Oh, Uncle Jim!"  Ann
leaned back against his arm to look at him in
surprise.

"Well, not real horns," laughed Uncle Jim.
"The things that look like horns are tufts of
feathers on the sides of his head.  They really
look more like a cat's ears than they do like horns.
In fact, when Mrs. Owl is huddled up on her nest
keeping her eggs warm, she looks surprisingly like
a nice brown-mottled Tabby Cat.

"The Great Horned Owl is about two feet long,
more than twice as big as the Screech Owl.  He

has big round yellow eyes that can see much better in the dark or dusk than in broad daylight.

"And it's in the dusk that the Horned Owl does his hunting. He glides through the air on his great wings as silently as a cloud floats across the face of the moon.

"You listen, tonight. Perhaps you'll hear him hooting."

Uncle Jim got up suddenly from his chair, lifting Ann up off the floor at the same time.

"And now," said he, "I have another idea, the best of all. Let's take the car and drive down to the Eagle Tree Hotel. There is a man at the hotel I want to see, and it's a lovely morning for a ride."

# What Hawks Eat

UNCLE JIM went out to get the car, and Ann ran after him, as gay as a frolicking puppy.

"Are we going by the place where you saw the Great Blue Heron?" she asked, watching him as he backed the car slowly out on the driveway.

"Not today," Uncle Jim turned the car around, heading away from the village. "We're going in another direction. But even if we don't see the Heron we'll see something interesting. You can be sure of that."

And it wasn't long before Ann, watching out of

141

the car window, did see something that made her exclaim and point with excitement. Suspended in the air above them was a bird with outspread wings. To Ann's eyes it seemed to be quite motionless, almost as if it were painted on the sky.

"Oh, look!" she cried. "Look up there, Uncle Jim. There's a bird that isn't going anywhere, or even flying at all. He just stays up all by himself! How can he?"

Uncle Jim pulled off his hat and leaned over Ann to look out of the window where she was pointing.

"That's a Hawk," he said, slowing down the car to get a better look. "A little Sparrow Hawk. He isn't going any place, but he's not perfectly still, either. His long wings are beating in quick short strokes so rapidly that they keep him up in the air, and he seems to be just hanging on nothing.

"He's the smallest of all our hawks, only ten inches long. He is waiting there looking for a grasshopper or a mouse on the field below. You wouldn't suppose he could see anything so small from away up so high, but he can. If a grasshopper hops or a field mouse runs, the hawk's sharp eyes will spy it, and that grasshopper, or that mouse is as good as eaten.

"The Sparrow Hawk is often called the Grasshopper Hawk. And that's really a better name for him, because he eats so many of these harmful insect pests.

"How he does love to eat them! Whenever he can find enough he actually stuffs himself with grasshoppers, eating a mouse or rat now and then for variety.

"Once in a while he will eat a little snake or frog, and again once in a while he will attack a small bird. But he takes birds so seldom that we shouldn't hold it against him. The Sparrow Hawk is really a good and useful bird."

"But people don't like Hawks very much, do

they, Uncle Jim?" questioned Ann, remembering some stories she had read. "Don't Hawks steal chickens?"

Uncle Jim rubbed his hand thoughtfully down the back of his head.

"Well," he said slowly, "Hawks do have a rather bad name, and some of them, like the Sharp-shinned Hawk, deserve that reputation. But I think it's a great mistake to think all Hawks are harmful. Some of them do much more good than harm. (See food chart on page 202.)

"The big Red-tailed Hawk, or Hen Hawk, will take a chicken every now and then, but he takes so many more rats and mice and frogs and moles and snakes that he is as much a friend as he is an enemy to the farmer."

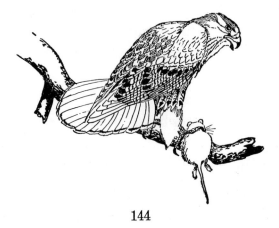

Uncle Jim started the car again and, about a mile farther along, he turned off from the main highway into a wooded road that wound gradually upward along a little, rippling brook.

"You've never been to the Eagle Tree Hotel, have you?" he said, changing into second gear as the road grew steeper.

"No," said Ann, "I haven't. Why do they call it that? It's a queer name for a hotel, don't you think so?"

"It doesn't seem queer to me," said Uncle Jim. "But then, I'm used to it. This is a summer hotel, you know, where people come on vacation because they want to be in the country. There's a very tall tree near by, and though I don't know that an Eagle ever had a nest in this particular tree, Eagles do build their nests in the tallest trees they can find. It was on account of this tree that the hotel people chose the name of 'Eagle Tree' for their hotel.

"There is an Eagle at the hotel, too, in a great big cage. That's what I brought you up here to see.

"The Big Bald Eagle is also called the American Eagle. He is our national emblem. You can

145

see him represented in any number of places. He's on the seal of the United States, and on dollar bills, and silver dollars and some other coins. Sometimes he's on the top of a flagpole.

"Well, now you're going to see this Eagle in person."

A sharp turn in the road brought them out in front of a long, rustic building with a wide veranda.

"Here we are," said Uncle Jim, slowing the car to a stop and jumping out. "I'll step into the office and speak to Mr. Ross for a minute, and then, if it's all right, we'll go around to the back of the hotel where the Eagle is. You had better wait here in the car. I won't be long."

## Our Own American Eagle

WHEN Uncle Jim came out of the hotel there was a smiling, white-haired man with him.

"This is my little niece Ann, Mr. Ross," he said, introducing Ann to the smiling man. "She would like to see your Bald Eagle."

"Why, of course," said Mr. Ross. "She must see the Eagle. He's one of the sights in this part of the country. I'll take you around to his cage."

The three of them walked around the end of the

hotel to the back, where a big cage had been built around a dead, bare tree. The cage was as large as a small room and high enough to take in a couple of branches of the tree.

On one of these branches sat a great bird nearly three feet long. He had a strongly hooked bill and a heavily feathered body of dark brown, with a white head, neck, and tail.

"Is that the Bald Eagle?" asked Ann.

"Yes, that's the Bald Eagle himself," said Mr. Ross.

"But he's not bald, not a bit."

Mr. Ross chuckled.

"No, he isn't bald, but that's his name just the same. I suppose, when he was flying around high up in the sky, his white head made him look bald to the people who named him. But it really isn't a very good name for him."

"I don't believe he likes it here in this cage, do you?" Ann looked questioningly at Mr. Ross.

"Well, I don't know," said Mr. Ross. "He's been here long enough to be used to it by this time."

"He doesn't like it, I know," broke in Uncle Jim. "How could he? It's against his nature.

*Eagles build their nests on high mountain peaks
and in the tops of tall trees.*

The Eagle is a wild, majestic bird, made to fly far and wide on his powerful wings high above the earth. Look at him now, caged up here. See how fiercely he looks at us."

Ann drew back a little from the cage.

"Would he hurt us, Uncle Jim, if he were outside?"

"Oh, no, I don't think so. He's been here such a long time, as Mr. Ross says, that he'd probably want to fly away as quickly as he could. He'd be satisfied if he were free and could soar up into the sky, higher and higher and higher, and then swoop down and catch up a fish to eat. He likes a dead one best.

"He has wonderful eyesight and can spot a dead fish on the shore, or floating on the water, from a mile or maybe two miles away. At that distance we shouldn't be able to see it at all, even if we used very strong field glasses."

They stood still and gazed at the Eagle, and the great bird closed its eyes as if it were bored.

"Well," remarked Uncle Jim, "I guess he has had enough of us. We'd better be on our way."

He turned to Mr. Ross. "Thank you very much," he said, putting his arm around Ann's shoulders to include her in his thanks, "for letting us see your Bald Eagle."

"Yes," said Ann. "I did want to see him. But I wouldn't want to have him any nearer, and I wouldn't like to have him mad at me, either. His claws look terribly strong and scratchy."

They turned to go back to the car, and just then, from behind them there sounded a soft, cooing, bird call, repeated two or three times.

A look of surprise came over Ann's face.

"My goodness!" she exclaimed, looking up at Uncle Jim. "Wouldn't you think a bird as big and fierce-looking as that Eagle would have a bigger voice than that?"

Both the men laughed.

"Turn around, Ann," said Uncle Jim, "and you'll see where that sound came from. It wasn't the Eagle. If it had been his call it would have been a loud, clear *Cac-cac-cac*, almost like a crazy man's laugh. Sometimes his call is almost like a scream."

Ann turned and saw on the ridge of the garage roof a pair of birds about twelve inches long. They were a soft gray in color, with beautiful rainbow-colored necks and rosy red feet.

"Mourning Doves," said Uncle Jim. "Those are the birds you heard. Aren't they lovely! And they are even more useful than they are lovely. Some people call the Mourning Dove the farmer's helper, because he eats so many harmful weed seeds.

"Once in a while he will eat a grasshopper or so along with the seeds, but in the main he greatly prefers a vegetable diet."

"Why is he mournful?" asked Ann.

"He isn't really mournful. That's only his name because the people who named him thought his soft call had a mournful sound.

"It doesn't sound sorrowful to me. You can

always recognize the gentle *coo-coo* of a Mourning Dove after you've once heard it.

"There is another sound he makes, which identifies him, too. That is the sharp whistling sound of his wings when he is flying. When several Mourning Doves are flying together, this whistling of their wings is easily heard."

"Are there any Mourning Doves around our house?" asked Ann.

"Oh, yes, there has been a pair of Doves around all summer. You can see Mourning Doves in ever so many places around the country.

"But we've taken too much of Mr. Ross's time this morning. So say good-by to him, Ann, and we will go to watch the Mourning Doves at home."

# The Polite Cedar Waxwing

"ANN! Ann!" called Uncle Jim, coming around the corner of the house. "Where are you, Ann?"

Then he saw her standing at the end of the garden under a tree looking at something she was holding in her half-closed hands.

At the sound of his call she turned toward him, and he saw marks of tears on her face. He hurried across the garden to her.

"Why, Ann, what is the matter?" he asked, with concern in his voice.

She opened her hands and showed him the limp body of a little dead bird. It was beautifully colored in soft shades of brownish gray, with velvety black around its eyes, and a band of clear lemon yellow at the end of its tail. On the tips of its wings there were some curious dots that looked like touches of bright red sealing wax.

"I found him lying right here on the ground," said Ann, with a catch in her voice. "And he's such a pretty bird. I wish he hadn't died. What kind is he?"

"A Cedar Waxwing shows his feelings with the crest of
feathers on his head the way a horse does with its ears."

"A Cedar Waxwing," said Uncle Jim, touching the soft feathers gently. "Those little wax-like spots give him his name.

"But don't feel bad about him. Instead, let us think that the part of him that was happy here has perhaps gone to some Happy Hunting Ground in Bird Heaven. Maybe he's having a wonderful time there this very minute, flying around among the trees and shrubs, and eating all the bugs, and inchworms, and wild cherries that he wants. And he wants a lot, for he has a big appetite.

"Let's take him over to the barn, and I'll tell you something about him."

Ann handed the Cedar Waxwing to Uncle Jim, and followed him into the barn. He laid the pretty bird on a big box.

"See that little crest of feathers on his head," he said. "A Cedar Waxwing shows his feelings with that crest the way a horse does with its ears. When he's calm and happy, the crest lies loosely on his head. When he is excited the feathers rise quickly erect, and if he's frightened the feathers are pressed closely against his head. You can tell how he is feeling by looking at his crest.

"The Cedar Waxwing has about the best manners of any bird I know. I once saw half a dozen of them sitting close together on a tree limb. They are very friendly birds, and often sit that way. One bird had a cherry in his bill. He didn't eat the cherry right down, as you'd expect a bird to do. He turned and passed it to the bird beside him, and that bird did the same to the one beside him, and so on all the way down the line and back again before one of them took a bite of the cherry.

"Now, don't you think that looks like politeness?"

"I didn't know birds ever did anything like that," said Ann with surprise.

"Oh, yes. And sometimes, when several Waxwings are sitting together, one bird will smooth the head and back plumage of another bird with his bill.

"I am very fond of Cedar Waxwings. I ought to be, because, one year, when we had a pest of inchworms eating the leaves of our apple trees, along came a flock of Waxwings and began eating the worms.

"They ate and ate and ate and ate till, actually, it would seem that they couldn't swallow a single worm more. But they saved our apple crop for us.

"After that we didn't grudge them the cherries they wanted. A Waxwing does like cherries. But he likes the wild black cherries in the woods even better than he likes cultivated fruit.

"One day last summer, I had a chance to see how much Cedar Waxwings really do like wild cherries. I was in the woods near a big black cherry tree at the time the cherries were about ripe. I noticed a great number of birds flying toward that tree. So I stayed to watch them a while. They weren't flying in flocks. They were sort of stringing along, two or three at a time. They were all Cedar Waxwings, some young birds and some old ones. There must have been two or three hundred of them.

"I walked over nearer to the tree to see what was going on. And you would have thought there was a hailstorm under that tree! The birds were all eating the wild cherries as fast as they could gulp them down, just making a business of cleaning up that cherry tree. And the cherry stones were dropping to the ground like rain or hailstones.

"Such a rattling downpour!

"Well, I watched them for a while, and then walked on.

"After I had gone a little way I happened to look back. I suppose they had eaten the last cherry, and were ready to move on. Anyway, there they were, pouring out of that tree like ... well, I couldn't think of anything but smoke pouring out of a big chimney.

"I could see them against the sky. The sun was setting, and they showed up plainly, black against the pink sunset. They seemed to be following a leader. They circled around a few times going higher and higher until they were above the tallest trees.

"Then they flew off on a straight line to some roosting place for the night."

Suddenly Uncle Jim snapped his fingers.

"Well, well!" he exclaimed. "Here I sit talking, and forgetting altogether that I came to tell you, you were going to have company."

"Company!" echoed Ann. "Who?"

"Young Jerry Williams. He lives just beyond the bridge, on the way to the village. I stopped there to see his father this morning, and I found Jerry finishing a little birdhouse he'd been making. He had made it so well, and it was such a nice little birdhouse, that I asked him to come along with me and show it to you."

"Why didn't he come?" Ann looked disappointed.

"He wasn't quite ready, and I didn't want to wait. But he'll be along any minute now."

Uncle Jim knocked the ashes from the pipe he had been smoking, and went over to the barn door to look down the road.

"There he is now, coming down the road; so rub the tear marks off your face, and have a smile for Jerry. He's a fine boy. You'll like him."

# Jerry's Wren House

JERRY came into the yard carrying the little
birdhouse carefully, in a manner that showed
his pride in it.

The house was quite small, only five by six
inches. He had made it beautifully, and had
painted it white with a green roof.

Uncle Jim called to him, and Jerry came over
to the barn.

"So you've brought it. That's good!" said Uncle Jim. "Jerry, this is Ann. I've been telling her about your birdhouse. Look, Ann, isn't that a fine piece of work?"

At Uncle Jim's words of praise, Jerry's wide-awake, freckled face lighted with a shy, but pleased smile. He shifted his weight from one foot to the other and, for a moment he couldn't seem to think of anything to say.

But Ann's delighted interest in his little house made him forget about being shy, and he began to explain its finer points to her.

"It's a Wren house," he said. "I made the entrance hole only one inch across." He turned the house so that she could see. "An inch is big enough for a little Wren to go in, but it's too small for an English Sparrow, and this way the Sparrows can't get inside to hurt the baby Wrens, the way they hurt the little Bluebirds.

"The floor unhooks. See." He showed her how it worked. "That's so the house can be cleaned out and made ready for a new nest, after one family is through with it.

"House Wrens nest in all sorts of funny places, but they like their nests to be *inside* something

162

and to have a cover over their heads, like this house, or a little hole in a tree. And they don't like to move in where there's been a dirty old nest, do they?"

Jerry looked at Uncle Jim for approval of this last remark.

"That's right," agreed Uncle Jim. "Jenny Wren is a fussy little housekeeper. Mr. Wren could tell you that, I'm sure. If he picks out a place for her to build a nest, and she doesn't like it she'll have nothing to do with it, or with him either. She'll get herself another husband who can find her a better house. She is really more interested in her house than she is in her husband.

"She doesn't like to have very near neighbors. If there is an empty Wren's nest in the same tree, or pretty close by, she will fill it up with little sticks or straws, to keep other Wrens out.

"She doesn't want to eat seeds. She wants bugs, and plenty of them. Since there aren't any more than enough insects in one place for her own hungry family, she does her best to keep other families away.

"Jenny Wren is something of a scold, too. She has a very sharp tongue when she is annoyed."

163

Uncle Jim paused and gave a little chuckle. "Jenny and I had a regular set-to, one time. I guess I'll have to tell you about it.

"One day I happened to stick my head up under the eaves of that little shed." He pointed to an old tool shed outside the barn. "I had seen a Wren flying in and out, and I had an idea I might find her nest. So I went to find out.

"Sure enough! There was Jenny sitting on her eggs. And I had broken right in upon her.

"Well! If you've ever heard anybody scold! She was so furious that before I even saw her she gave an angry scream right in my ear. It startled me so I bumped my head on the edge of the roof, and in Wren language she started in to tell me what she thought of me. 'You nosey old thing!' she cried. 'Can't you mind your own business and keep out of here! Can't we have any privacy! What's this to you anyhow? Haven't you room enough outside?'

"And she kept on giving me a piece of her mind, even after I had gone. I got away in a hurry, too, I can tell you."

The children laughed at the idea of big Uncle Jim being frightened by a little Wren. And Uncle Jim laughed, too, but he rubbed his head as if he still felt that bump. Then he went on talking.

"She scolds Mr. Wren in much the same way, only he doesn't pay any attention to her scolding. He sits outside somewhere and cocks his tail over his head and keeps singing his bubbling, merry tune all day long, no matter what she says to him."

Uncle Jim stood up.

"But I don't know why we should be keeping

ourselves hidden in this dark barn," he said. "Let's put your birdhouse up on this shelf where it will be safe, Jerry, and go outside. It seemed to me I smelled something like ginger cookies baking, when I came by the kitchen door. Some fresh cookies and milk wouldn't be so bad, would they?"

The idea seemed a very good one to Ann and Jerry, and before many minutes had passed they were sitting comfortably on the back porch. There was a plate of warm ginger cookies between them and a glass of milk for each of them.

After eating quietly for a little while, Jerry began to talk again.

"Did you ever see a Belted Kingfisher, Ann?" he asked, between bites of his cooky.

"No," said Ann. "What's a Kingfisher like?"

"It's a bird about the size of a Flicker, maybe a little bigger. It's sort of gray-blue on top and white underneath. It has a big tousled head and a big long bill.

"I saw one this morning when I was crossing the bridge on my way here. I stopped to watch him. He was sitting on a branch that stuck out over the water about ten feet up. I guess he

must have seen a fish in the water down below, because he dropped off that branch and went *plunk!* right down into the water. Then he came up with a squirmy minnow in his bill. You ought to have seen him."

"I wish I had," said Ann. "Did he eat the fish then?"

"No, I thought he was going to eat it, but he didn't. He took it and flew to a hole in the sandy bank at the edge of the brook, and disappeared into the hole. I guess he had a nest in there."

"Do you mean he fed the fish to the baby birds?" Ann looked at Jerry with doubt.

"Yes, of course. That's what they eat and that's how they got the name of Kingfishers."

"Oh." Ann finished her glass of milk slowly. "Did you see anything else?" she asked.

"Nothing much. I saw some Red-winged Blackbirds in the swamp. They're pretty, and I like to hear them sing, but they're no special treat. You can see them around here in swamps most anywhere. Some of the farmers don't like them much, because they say Redwings eat the grain.

"But my father says they eat a whole lot more weed seeds than grain, and that they do more good than harm. And my father ought to know. He's a farmer, too."

*Mockingbird*

# A Hundred Songs

JERRY swallowed the last bite of his last cooky, and looked over at Ann. She was finishing her last cooky, too.

Jerry was having a good time. The cookies had been very good, and plentiful. He had enjoyed the praises his birdhouse had received, and he had enjoyed Ann's eager interest in what he had been telling her. She was such a good listener. He thought he'd like to tell her something more about birds.

He began, as before, with a question.

"Did you ever hear a Mockingbird sing?" he asked her.

"No," said Ann. "I never did."

"Well," announced Jerry, "I heard a Mocking-bird last night singing his head off, and you don't often hear one of them around here."

"You don't hear what?" asked Uncle Jim coming out of the house onto the porch.

"Mockingbirds," replied Jerry. "I heard one last night." He hesitated for a moment. "Any-way, I was pretty sure I did."

"I guess you did then," said Uncle Jim, looking at Jerry with a smile. "They come around here once in a while. It was a bright moonlight night, and Mockingbirds often sing at night.

"It was warm too. Maybe he thought he was in the South. He's a real southern bird, and that's where you can hear him at his best. He is a wonderful singer. He has a hundred songs, and he sings them all well. He imitates, or mocks, the songs of other birds. That's how he got his name. He will even imitate the sounds that come from a radio or a piano, and do it pretty well, too. I once heard a Mockingbird mimic a dog's bark.

"Mockingbirds are quite dull in their coloring, gray or brownish gray above, and pale smoky-

170

gray underneath. They have rather long tails. If they are treated well, they will grow to be quite friendly and nest near the house. We have a good many birds in our garden, but I wish we had some Mockingbirds too. They sing so beautifully."

Uncle Jim turned his eyes toward the garden as he spoke. Then he lowered his voice and pointed over toward the lilac bushes.

"Look!" he said. "Though we don't have a Mockingbird, we do have his cousin, the Brown Thrasher, and there is one now."

The children looked in the direction of his pointing finger. On the ground near the lilacs they saw a cinnamon-brown bird about eleven inches long with a buffy-white breast, streaked with dark brown, or black, a good deal like a Thrush's breast.

"But the Brown Thrasher isn't a Thrush at all," declared Uncle Jim when Ann spoke of the likeness. "He belongs to the Mockingbird family."

"Why is he called a Thrasher?" asked Ann, keeping her eyes on the brown bird as she spoke.

"Because he thrashes, or switches, his tail about," added Jerry. "Watch him."

And true enough, the bird did switch his tail as he flew up on the limb of a tree and started to sing.

They all stood still and listened to the Brown Thrasher's song.

"He doesn't sing quite so beautifully as his Mockingbird cousin," said Uncle Jim. "And he doesn't sing so much. But he has a very nice song of his own.

"We often see the Brown Thrasher scratching around on the ground among the dry leaves looking for insects and worms. We like to have him here. But he doesn't care to nest as close to human beings as the Mockingbird does."

While they were watching him, the Brown Thrasher finished his song, and with a final switch of his tail he flew away.

"There he goes," said Ann.

172

"Yes, but he'll come back and sing to you again sometime," said Uncle Jim. "The Mockingbird has another cousin, too, that we see around here quite often. Jerry knows him, don't you, Jerry?"

"Catbird," grinned Jerry. "'Yeh! Yeh!'"

Ann's forehead wrinkled into a puzzled little frown. "What do you mean, 'Yeh! Yeh!'?"

Jerry grinned again.

"That's one of his calls, sort of snarly, like a cross cat. Catbird — don't you see?"

"But that's not a bit like a Mockingbird," objected Ann.

"Oh, he has a song too, a nice one, when he wants to sing it. But he keeps interrupting himself with his cat calls and yowls.

*Catbird*

"He's a sort of copy cat, like his cousins, isn't he?"

Jerry turned to Uncle Jim for his approval.

"Yes," replied Uncle Jim. "The Catbird copies other bird songs, as the Mockingbird does, but you can always know a Catbird's song because he gives himself away by those little cat calls."

"What does he look like?" asked Ann.

"He's mostly slate-gray in color, but he has a black crown, and black on his wings and tail. And like his cousins, the Mockingbird and the Brown Thrasher, his tail is quite long."

Ann listened while Uncle Jim described the Catbird. Then she turned to Jerry. "Did you know that too?" she asked him.

"Why yes," said Jerry. "Catbirds are common. I've seen lots of them."

"Oh," said Ann again.

Then she turned her thoughts to something else.

"What'll we do now?" she said, hopping up and down on one foot and looking questioningly at Jerry.

But it was Uncle Jim who answered her.

"Wait a minute," he said. "I came out here to give Jerry a telephone message from his father.

174

It's too bad to break up your fun, but your father says he wants you for something at home, Jerry."

Jerry looked disappointed.

"Well," he said slowly. "I guess I'll have to go then. He told me not to stay too long."

"Never mind," smiled Uncle Jim. "You can come again. I tell you what I'll do. I'll take out the car and drive you and your birdhouse home. We'll all go. How's that?"

"Fine!" said Ann and Jerry together, and they both started racing toward the garage to see which one would reach there first.

# The Sparrow Family

UNCLE JIM was sitting in the shade of the barn on an old box. Ann sat beside him watching with interest as he whittled away at a little whistle he was making for her.

All of a sudden through the warm sunny air came a burst of lovely bird song. Ann started to her feet to see where it came from, but Uncle Jim pulled her back.

The Song Sparrow is a native American bird.
He sings almost as well as the Canary.

The Slate-colored Junco comes and stays all winter.

"Quiet, quiet!" he said in a low voice. "Never make a quick motion when you want to see a bird. Don't move at all if you can help it, but if you do move do it very slowly. If you jump up suddenly you will frighten away almost any bird."

"I wanted to see what sort of bird was singing," explained Ann.

"Yes, I know, but don't jump at him like that. It's a Song Sparrow. He's there across the yard on the top of a lilac bush. Can you see?"

A smallish bird streaked with brown and black was singing with all his heart from the topmost twig of the bush. His little head was thrown back and the music was pouring from his throat. His

breast was white with dark wedge-shaped little streaks all over it, and he had a good-sized dark spot right in the center of the streaks.

"A Song Sparrow!" exclaimed Ann in surprise. "I didn't suppose a Sparrow could sing like that. I thought Sparrows weren't very nice birds, anyway."

"You're thinking of an English Sparrow," corrected Uncle Jim, "and he's quite a different bird. The English Sparrow was brought over here from Europe. He is what people sometimes call an 'Undesirable Alien.'"

Ann pushed back the thick hair that was forever falling into her eyes.

"What is an Undesirable Alien?" she asked.

"He is someone from another country who comes here and does no good to anybody. People wish he'd stayed at home. They send him back if they can.

"But we can't send back the English Sparrow. There are millions of them here now.

"The Song Sparrow is a native American bird. He's a very nice bird indeed, and everybody likes him. He doesn't do any harm to any other bird. He eats little bugs and many, many weed seeds.

178

And, in addition, he sings almost as well as a Canary.

"But don't ever confuse the Song Sparrow with the rowdy English Sparrow."

"I won't," said Ann. "I didn't know the difference, but now I do."

She drew her feet up under her and hugged her knees.

"I guess the Song Sparrow wouldn't like to be taken for an Undesirable Alien, would he?" She smiled at Uncle Jim.

"Not at all," said Uncle Jim soberly. He smoothed off the end of the whistle and went on talking.

"There are several kinds of native Sparrows," he said. "The Chipping Sparrow is one of the best known, and one of the best loved. Chippy is little, only about five and a half inches long, but he isn't afraid to hop almost up to your feet. He is a friendly, trusting little chap.

"And he's very useful too. He is death to cabbage worms and grasshoppers. And it's good-by wasp, if he happens to see one. He also eats quantities of weed seeds.

"The Chipping Sparrow has a little chestnut-colored crown, and a narrow black stripe that runs from his bill right across his eye and beyond; and he sings, *Chip-chip-chip-chip!*"

Uncle Jim stopped talking for a minute, as he carefully cut a mouthpiece on the little whistle. Then he went on again.

"The Field Sparrow looks a good deal like the Chipping Sparrow, only he has a pinkish brown bill, much redder than that of his cousin Chippy. He doesn't come around the house so much, either. He prefers the fields.

"Field Sparrows build their nests among the grasses or weeds on the ground. They make them of dry weed stems and grasses and of little strips of bark.

"One time in the early spring I saw a Field Sparrow beginning her nest. It was the prettiest sight you can think of. She took a long piece of dead grass, about... oh, maybe a foot and a half long. And at every half inch or so she would pinch it with her bill, not hard enough to break it, but just enough so that she could bend it around to work it into her nest."

"Oh, Uncle Jim!" Ann twisted herself around on the box. "Why can't I see things like that?"

"You can," said Uncle Jim, "if you keep on watching. Remember, I have been looking at birds a good many years longer than you have."

"Yes," said Ann, "I suppose so. Are there any other Sparrows?"

"Yes, there's the White-throated Sparrow that has a lovely song, only we don't hear him or see him quite so often.

"And there are ever so many other native Sparrows. Some of them look a good deal alike. You have to watch closely to tell them apart. Your bird book will show you the differences.

*A Field Sparrow building a nest*

"But you can always tell the Song Sparrow by that one larger spot in the center of his breast, and you can always tell the Chipping Sparrow by his chestnut-colored crown."

Uncle Jim had finished the whistle he had been making. He handed it to Ann.

"There," he said, shutting up his knife. "Now see what you can do with that. Maybe you can whistle some sort of bird call that will make the birds think you are a strange kind of big bird."

Ann laughed and blew softly through the whistle.

"Do I sound like a bird?" She blew again.

"M-m-m-m." Uncle Jim thought for a moment. "I think," he said slowly, "that you sound exactly like a nice Ann Bird."

She laughed again and gave him a hug. "I know quite a lot about birds now, don't I?" she said, looking up at him.

Uncle Jim slipped his knife back into his pocket.

"Yes," he said. "You have seen a good many and you'll see a good many more. There are ever so many more kinds of birds, you know."

Ann's face sobered suddenly.

"Y-e-s," she said slowly. "But I'm afraid I

won't see them, because vacation's almost over, and I'll have to be going back to the city."

While Ann had been talking, Uncle Jim had been looking across the field at a tall tree with widespread, leafless branches. He turned his glance away from the tree and looked at her.

"Never mind," he said, smiling. "A great many of the birds will be going away, too." Then he pointed towards the tree he had been watching. "Look over there, Ann! There's something for you to see!"

She looked. It was a surprising sight. Hundreds and hundreds of birds were circling gracefully around in the sky above the tall bare tree, making a sort of gurgling twitter as they flew. Then suddenly, as if they were obeying a signal, they all settled down upon the branches of the tree.

One by one they perched, squeezing in close beside each other till they sat strung out along the bare spreading branches as close together as if they were beads upon a string. The tree was almost covered with birds.

In a minute or two more, up they flew again like soldiers under orders, and began circling as before.

"What are they doing?" asked Ann, amazed. "What's happening? What birds are they?"

"Purple Martins. They are flocking, getting ready to leave. A great many birds, in fact most of them, migrate, you know. That is, they go away for the winter to a warmer climate. The Purple Martin is among the earliest of the birds to go. He is one of the Swallow family, and everybody likes to have him around. But he eats almost nothing but flying insects, and he has to go where there are plenty of insects for him to eat in the winter. He'd die if he stayed here.

"Don't you know our Martin house? It's the biggest one we have. It has several doors in it.

184

Martins are quite different from Wrens. Martins like to have neighbors. They don't need to find their food close to their nests. Their wings are so strong they can fly far and high in the air to get a bug, or they can skim along close to the ground to catch an insect. Their wings are like oars. The tail acts as a rudder and the birds can make a swift turn to capture a darting little insect.

"Some Martin houses are large enough so that ten or a dozen families can live in the different apartments in one birdhouse. They often return, year after year, to the same nesting place if it is made nice and clean for them.

"The Purple Martin is a beautiful and useful bird. But a funny thing about him is that he isn't purple at all. He's a lovely, deep, smoky blue."

## Graceful as a Swallow

ALL Swallows are graceful," said Uncle Jim, getting up from the box where he had been sitting. "But there's none so graceful as the Barn Swallow."

He looked up into the sky and then back into the barn.

"We ought to see a Barn Swallow around here almost any time. They come back, year after year, to build their nests in the same places.

"We have some Barn Swallows in our barn. I've seen them coming and going all summer."

He shaded his eyes and looked toward the sun again.

"There's one, now, flying over the field. See how beautifully he glides and soars and dips! And every time he dips and darts he catches and eats some flying insect. He catches all his food while he is flying, and he is almost always on the wing.

"I couldn't begin to tell you how many mosquitoes and flies and moths a Barn Swallow gets away with, but it is an enormous number. He's after them all the time."

"I can hear him," said Ann, turning her head to keep the Swallow in sight. "I can hear him. Can you? Is that a song he's singing?"

"Well, it is what he means for a song. It sounds more like a twittering, rippling little laugh, doesn't it? He keeps up that twitter a good deal of the time.

"Isn't he lovely? His back is such a shiny, dark, steel-blue, and his throat and under body such a pretty, shaded, brownish pink. It's a beautiful sight to see a flock of Barn Swallows wheeling and diving through the air, skimming over fields or dipping down into the smooth surface of a pond to catch a drink of water without stopping at all. You can almost feel how they love to fly."

"It's sort of like the way I feel when I'm skating, don't you think?" suggested Ann.

"I guess it must be something like that," said Uncle Jim, following the Swallow's graceful flight with his eyes.

"And did you notice his long, forked tail? The Barn Swallow has the longest tail of any of the Swallows, and the most deeply forked. That long, forked tail is what gave the name of 'swallow-tail' to the long-tailed coats men wear with their dress suits."

Ann chuckled. "So when you go to a party you dress like a Swallow."

"Like a Barn Swallow," corrected Uncle Jim. "The other Swallows don't have such deeply forked tails.

"But Barn Swallows aren't the only Swallows nesting around the barn. Several families of Cliff Swallows have their nests under the eaves on the other side of the barn. Come, I'll show you."

Uncle Jim led the way around to the other side

of the barn and pointed up to some odd-looking, jug-shaped clumps of dried mud under the over-hanging edges of the barn roof.

"There they are," he said. "The Cliff Swallows' nests."

"Those?" said Ann, surprised. "Are those funny things nests? They look more like fat little mud bottles or jugs, and they have only a tiny hole for the mother bird to come in and out."

"I know. But the Cliff Swallows built those funny gourd-shaped nests to suit themselves.

They like them. The nests are made of tiny mud balls stuck together while the mud is still wet. Then they are lined with straw and feathers so that they will be soft and comfortable for the baby birds.

"The first Cliff Swallows' nests that were discovered, long ago, by some explorers, were found plastered against the sides of high cliffs. There were hundreds of these nests close together. You can still find Cliff Swallows' nests in such places, but nowadays a great many of these Swallows seem to prefer to build under the eaves of a barn or other building where there is shelter from the rain. Too much rain might wash the mud nests away.

"A Cliff Swallow has a much shorter tail than any of his cousin Swallows. Like them he is a great eater of flying insects, and he gets along very well with his relatives. Sometimes where there are large numbers of mosquitoes and flies you can see three or four different kinds of Swallows. You can see Barn Swallows, Cliff Swallows, Tree Swallows, and Bank Swallows all in one large flock, and all busy cleaning the air of these flying pests."

Ann looked up at the Swallows' nests and put her whistle up to her mouth.

"What will the Swallows do if they hear me blow this?" she asked.

"Nothing," said Uncle Jim. "For I don't suppose there are any birds in those nests. They must have all gone by this time."

Ann blew softly on her whistle, but not a bird showed its head.

"I guess they have gone," she said. "I should think they would want to get out of those funny nests."

They walked slowly back to the house, while Uncle Jim went on talking.

"There is another bird," he said, "that does his part in helping to rid the air of flying bugs. He's the Chimney Swift. Like the Swallows, he too catches his food on the wing. And the name *Swift* is a good one for him, because he flies always at high speed. I've heard it said that he is able to go as fast as a hundred miles an hour.

"Back and forth he skims like a little airplane. He never seems to get tired or to rest at all in the daytime.

"A Swift's feet are so weak that he doesn't

seem to be able to grasp a branch with them, so that he can perch the way other birds do.

"At night he disappears into a hollow tree, or a chimney. There he rests by clinging to the inside of the tree, or the chimney wall, and by propping himself against the side with his stiff, stubby tail.

"A Chimney Swift's nest is built inside a chimney. It is cemented to the wall with a kind of glue that comes from the Swift's mouth. The nest hangs against the wall like a wall pocket or vase.

"And there is one very strange thing about Chimney Swifts. When they go away for the winter they just disappear.

"We know pretty well where the other birds

go when they migrate. But the Chimney Swifts, when autumn comes, gather their families together and fly southward, catching their food as they fly, and lodging at night in tall chimneys. Other birds of their own kind join them on the way until, by the time they reach the Gulf of Mexico, they have become a great army.

"Then suddenly they all disappear.

"And no one has yet been able to find out where it is they go."

# A Great Adventure

IT WAS evening. The sun had just slipped out of sight, leaving a sky all red and gold. Against the sky a row of maple trees on the hill stood out, in the clear evening air, like silhouettes cut from crisp black paper.

Uncle Jim leaned against one of the porch pillars enjoying the sunset and his evening pipe. Ann sat on the porch below him looking rather sober.

"I have to go away," she said, "like the birds. Only they want to go, and I don't."

Uncle Jim took his pipe out of his mouth.

"I don't know that they do want to go," he said thoughtfully. "But it isn't a matter of choice with them, anyway. They go because they must.

"The birds that live on insects, especially flying insects, would starve in the winter if they stayed up North, because the flies and mosquitoes and grasshoppers and bugs that swarm around in the fields and woods all summer disappear in the winter. The frost kills some of them, and others hide in the ground or under stones or behind the bark of trees. That makes this kind of bird food very scarce.

"But it isn't the lack of food alone that makes the birds migrate. They must have food, of course, but they leave while their food is still plentiful, long before they would have to go on account of hunger.

"Perhaps, as the days grow shorter, and the fall nights are longer, some birds may want longer hours of daylight to hunt all the food they need. But some of them go very early.

"You remember we saw the Purple Martins getting ready to leave, some time ago.

"And it can't be entirely on account of cold weather, either. It isn't cold yet, and a good many birds have already gone.

"There seems to be some special sense in the bird that tells him when it is time for him to go. Just as it tells him when it is time to come back North again, and to choose a mate, and to build a nest."

Uncle Jim put his pipe back in his mouth and began to draw on it, but it had gone out. He struck a match and lighted it. When it was going nicely he sat down on the step beside Ann.

"You might think," he said, "that after a long,

hard trip, when they had reached a nice warm place somewhere, they would stay there. But no. The next spring they start right back again on the long return journey, back to the same place they left in the fall."

"Where do they go?" asked Ann. "You said you knew where the birds went. I mean all, except the Chimney Swift."

"They go to a good many different places. Some don't go very far, and some go tremendous distances. The Arctic Tern goes the farthest of all. He flies all the way from the Arctic to the Antarctic Circle! But most of the birds go to warmer places. Some stop in Florida. Some go to Mexico, and some to Central America. Some go all the way to South America. And it's some of the littlest birds that fly the greatest distances."

"How do they know where to go? How do they find their way?"

"That," said Uncle Jim, "is a hard question to answer. I don't believe anybody can answer it entirely. Birds have wonderful eyesight, but that isn't the answer, because a great many of them travel at night when they can't see any landmarks.

And a great many fly over large bodies of water where they are out of sight of land, or of anything to show them the way.

"It is an amazing thing that they *do* know when to go and where to go. And it is just as amazing that, months later, they can return by the same route and reach the exact spot where they were the year before. Again it must be that special sense that guides them.

"Some birds, like Swallows, travel by day catching their food as they fly, and resting when it is dark. These birds follow the coast around the west end of the Gulf of Mexico where they can find plenty of insects.

"But most of the other birds fly by night. They go in big flocks, usually. They rest and eat in the daytime when they can see to get their food, and they journey at night.

"A number of them go South through Florida, and on to South America by way of Cuba and Jamaica. But the greatest number, oh, millions of them, fly directly across the Gulf of Mexico. This means that they must make a single flight of from five hundred to seven hundred miles."

"Do you mean," broke in Ann, "that they

fly straight across the Gulf of Mexico without stopping anywhere?"

"Yes. Where could they stop? There's no place to rest. They must go all the way, once they've started. They stay on the coast only long enough to take in a good supply of food and then, at the close of day, they start out boldly across the Gulf. They make the long crossing in a single night, flying at very high speed."

"Oh-h-h!" Ann shivered. "Wouldn't you think they'd be afraid, in the dark over all that water?"

"They're not afraid. Even the tiny Humming-bird flies more than five hundred miles, and it doesn't seem to worry him, at all. He is ready to do it all over again on his way North the next spring."

Ann sat still, thinking of that long, dark ocean flight. Then a new thought came to her.

"But, Uncle Jim," she said, "all the birds don't go away, do they?"

"Oh, no. The Nuthatches and Titmice and little Chickadees and some others stay around all winter. And some birds from Canada and from places north of this migrate down here.

"And when so many of our summer birds have left us, the little Slate-colored Junco comes and stays with us all winter long. (See color photograph opposite page 176.)

"He is a neat-looking bird, slate-gray above and white underneath. His bill is a light pinkish color, and he has two white outer tail feathers that flash into sight when he flies.

"We can see him dodging busily in and out of the bushes in the garden, day after day, or hopping around on the ground looking for weed seeds, or maybe a caterpillar, if it isn't too cold for a caterpillar to be out.

"And all the time he keeps up a pleasant, contented little chatter.

"When snow comes and covers up the weed seeds, we put out crumbs and seeds for the Junco so that he won't be hungry. He's quite friendly. He isn't afraid to come right up to the door to eat. I think everybody likes the Junco, and likes to have him around. When I was a boy we used to call him the 'Snowbird' and we were always glad to see him come."

Ann gave a regretful little sigh. "I wish that I could see him too," she said.

"You can," said Uncle Jim, putting his arm around her. "If you come to visit us in your Christmas holidays, you can see the Junco and feed him yourself.

"And after that it won't be very long before we wake up some pleasant morning and see a Robin on the lawn, or hear a Bluebird's cheery warble telling us that winter is over.

"Then before you know it, the trees will begin putting out their new green leaves, and all the birds will come flying back to us again."

Ann smiled up at Uncle Jim and gave the arm that was around her a quick little squeeze.

"And I'll be coming back too," she said.

*The little Junco*

# RED-TAILED HAWK or *Hen Hawk*

Rats and Mice
55.

Insects 10.5

Rabbits, Squirrels 9.3

Small Birds 9.2

Poultry 6.3

Frogs, Snakes 6.1

Game Birds 2.1
Aquatic 1.5

# SPARROW HAWK or *Grasshopper Hawk*

Insects
63.5

Rats and Mice
20.3

Small Birds 8.4

Frogs, Snakes 7.8

## FOOD CHARTS OF HAWKS

The Red-tailed Hawk eats about five times as many rats and mice as grasshoppers. The Sparrow Hawk eats about three times as many grasshoppers as rats and mice.

# How to Use the Index

THE index in this book lists all the birds that the book tells about. Under the name of each bird are lists of the things told about that bird with the pages on which the information can be found.

For example, to find out what kind of food Hawks eat, look for the words that begin with *H*. Run your finger down the column until you come to the word *Hawk*.

The index says:

**Hawks.** *See:*
    Red-tailed Hawk
    Sharp-shinned Hawk
    Sparrow Hawk

This shows that the book tells about three kinds of Hawks. You must look up each of these names to find what the different Hawks eat. Begin with the Red-tailed Hawk. Look for the words that begin with *R*, and find *Red-tailed Hawk*. Under it is this list of words in alphabetical order.

    food, 144, 202
    picture, 144

Find the word *food*. The numbers after it show the pages on which the book tells about the food the Red-tailed Hawk eats.

Write the word *Red-tailed Hawk* on a piece of paper with the page numbers about food. As you read those pages, make a list of the things the Hawk eats. Do this for each of the three Hawks.

If you want to know something about a certain bird's *nest*, look for that bird's name and find the word *nest*. If the word *nest* is not there, you will know that the book does not tell anything about that bird's nest.

To find out about the size, shape, and color of a bird look under the word *description*.

To find out about the different ways a bird acts or behaves, how it moves about, and in what sort of places it lives, look under the word *habits*.

The book also tells about the family some of the birds belong to and about their *eggs* and *young*.

# Index

207

**Red-breasted**
        **Nuthatch,** 11

**Red-eyed Vireo**
  description, 125, 126
  habits, 125
  name, 126
  song, 126

**Red-headed**
        **Woodpecker**
  description, 7
  food, 8, 9
  picture, 7

**Redstart**
  (*Warbler family*)
  description, 83
  female, 83
  habits, 83, 84
  migration, 84
  picture, 83

**Red-tailed Hawk**
  food, 144, 202
  picture, 144

**Red-winged Blackbird**
  description, 168
  food, 168
  picture, 168
  song, 168

**Reed Bird**
  *See:* Bobolink

**Rice Bird**
  *See:* Bobolink

**Robin**
  (*Thrush family*)
  care of young, 3, 4,
    5, 18, 19
  color photograph,
    opposite title page
  description, 3
  eggs, 21
  female, 3, 4, 20
  food, 1, 3, 4, 6, 20
  male, 22
  nest, 3, 20
  picture, 1, 18, 20, 23

**Rose-breasted**
        **Grosbeak**
  (*Finch family*)
  description, 41
  food, 42, 43
  habits, 42
  picture, 41
  song, 42

**Ruby-crowned Kinglet**
  *See:* Kinglets

213